*Julie*

"It's a Long Way to Tipperary"

# "It's a Long Way to Tipperary"

# British and Irish Nurses in the Great War

## Yvonne McEwen

Cualann Press

ISBN-10: 0-9544416-5-6
ISBN-13: 978-0-9544416-5-4

First Edition 2006

British Library Cataloguing in Publication Data. A catalogue record of this book is available at the British Library.

Printed by
Bell & Bain Ltd

Published by
Cualann Press Limited
6 Corpach Drive
Dunfermline
KY12 7XG
Scotland
Tel/Fax +44 (0)1383 733724
Email: info@cualann.com
Website: www.cualann.com

# Acknowledgements

Had it not been for the support of loved ones, friends and colleagues I am not altogether convinced that I would have taken on and completed the time-consuming task of writing this book. I have spent the best part of a year explaining how busy I am, leaving little or no time for the warmth and enjoyment that comes from special relationships. Please accept my apologies for not being immediately appreciative of good intentions and unstinting support; you have been central to my motivation and never far from my thoughts.

For encouragement and help, my thanks go to Susan McGann, Archivist, at the Royal College of Nursing, and Co-Director of the United Kingdom Centre for the History of Nursing. I am indebted to the staff of the Imperial War Museum, Department of Documents, London, The National Archives, London, the National Army Museum, London, the National Library of Scotland, Edinburgh, the Public Record Office of Northern Ireland, the National Library of Ireland, Dublin, the Allen Library, Dublin, Milford Library, Milford, County Donegal, The University of Edinburgh, Special Collections Department and the Centre for the Study of Two World Wars, for their help, courtesy and patience .

While researching the lives of Sisters Luard, Black and Peterkin, I was fortunate to receive help and guidance from members of their families. I would like to thank them for their generosity of time and support. I hope I have done justice to the memory of their loved ones. It is also fitting that I thank Geoff Russell Grant and Eric Hall, from Birch, who very diligently and enthusiastically responded to my requests for information about Evelyn Luard, and her family.

I would like to acknowledge the support of copyright holders and trustees of quoted material which has been invaluable: the Trustees of the Imperial War Museum for the use of the papers and diaries of Reverend Mother Georgine, Miss Bickmore, Miss Clarke and Miss Peterkin; the Imperial War Museum Sound Archive for the use of Margaret Warren's interview; the National Army Museum for permission to quote from the diaries of Lord Roberts; the Deputy Keeper of Records, the Public Record Office Northern Ireland for the use of the Maxwell papers; The National Archives for authorisation to quote from various papers held in their collection; the Allen Library, Dublin, for the use of witness statements from the Easter Rising; the Orion Publishing Group for permission to quote from *General Jack's Diary,* by John Terraine and published by Cassell; and to Birlinn Limited for permission to quote from *The Great Push* by Patrick MacGill. Every effort has been made to track down and contact copyright holders but if there have been omissions I apologise. Any omissions that come to light will be acknowledged in future editions.

Finally, I want to thank Dr Paul Addison who over the past few years has given me guidance, encouragement and wisdom. I extend my heartfelt gratitude to Sheila Crilly for her skill, counsel and friendship. For the last twenty years she has reviewed my written work and has made valuable suggestions for amendments, this book being no exception. To Alistair, who has shown remarkable restraint at my inability to understand the workings of the computer, I say, 'Thank you for your patience, forbearance and tremendous input into this book; your skills are many and have not always been openly or readily appreciated by me.' Last, but by no means least, my thanks to dear Ben, whose unconditional love and acceptance has brought a reality check to many trying days – all he wanted were long walks along the river bank.

The sister wraps my bandage again,
Oh, gentle the sister's hand,
But the smart of a restless longing, vain,
She cannot understand.

......

The ward-fire burns in a cheery way,
A vision in every flame,
There are books to read and games to play
But oh! for an old, old game,
With glancing bay-net and trusty gun
And wild blood bursting free!
But an arm is crippled, a leg is gone,
And the game's no more for me.

Extracts from 'The Everyday of War'
(Hospital, Versailles, November, 1915.)
*Soldier Songs* by Patrick MacGill, Herbert Jenkins 1916
(Writer, poet and Great War stretcher-bearer)

## Biographical Note

Yvonne McEwen is an Honorary Fellow at The University of Edinburgh Centre for the Study of Two World Wars where she is currently researching endurance and survival in combatants. She was previously an Honorary Research Fellow at the Institute of Irish Studies at The University of Liverpool working on Ireland's involvement in Two World Wars. She is a graduate of The University of Edinburgh with degrees in nursing and history.

# Contents

# Introduction

This is a book about the human face of warfare: endurance, survival, comradeship and the indominability of the human spirit. It is about the men who fought in the Great War and the women who nursed those who became its casualties. It is written in a spirit of remembrance for the unselfish, unstinting commitment to humanity that many nurses, both professional and volunteer, demonstrated while serving on the Western Front.

The role that British and Irish professional nurses played between 1914 and 1918 has been almost completely ignored, not only by the nursing profession, but by historians generally. For the most part, the history of women ministering to the sick and injured during this period has focused on Voluntary Aid Detachment nurses (VAD or volunteer nurses). Professional nurses, women who trained as nurses prior to the outbreak of the war, are seldom represented in the Great War historical literature. This book is primarily about their war. Since the publication in 1980 of Lyn MacDonald's book, *The Roses of No Man's Land*, there have been few British or Irish writings on the subject of nursing in the Great War. Vera Brittain, who detailed her days as a wartime volunteer nurse in *Testament of Youth*, became the public's perception of a wartime nurse. The writers Agatha Christie and Naomi Mitchison, both VAD nurses during the war, reflected their own wartime nursing experiences in their later writings, but they did not convey the war's full horrors and the demands on nurses.

Over the years, nurses of the Great War have been depicted as young, pretty and upper-class. While the image of young, innocent, self-sacrificing ladies of good social position ministering to the war wounded might appear attractive, the reality was that they were only part of the picture as, for the most part, the women who nursed in, and managed the Casualty Clearing Stations, Base Hospitals, Hospital Barges and Trains were over thirty, middle-class, determined, dedicated, trained professionals.

While researching the health implications of active service on trained and volunteer nurses and the causes of their deaths, it was surprising to find that no official Great War archive existed and no research had been carried out into the personal consequences of war work on British and Irish nurses. I have tried to establish the number of British, Irish and Dominion nurses killed between 1914 and 1918. In relation to in-service war deaths, likely sources such as the Royal College of Nursing (RCN) and the Imperial War Museum were approached but neither had firm data that could be used as evidence. The absence of detail in the RCN archive, compiled several years after the war, was disturbing. The Imperial War Museum had no list of war-related deaths within the various nursing corps but, after consulting the Commonwealth War Graves Commission and cross referencing the names of female casualties who died in the Great War with military records, newspapers and various publications, it was possible to establish the number of deaths that took place in the various nursing divisions. The outcome of this research was illuminating and some of the findings are incorporated into this book in a Roll of Honour. The work is ongoing and I have recently found the names of a further thirty nurses who died while on active service but, for the moment, there is little information on their ages, designations, corps and the areas of military operation where they nursed.

I have limited the scope of the book to nursing activities on the Western Front for three reasons. Firstly, France and Flanders were the main theatres of military operations, secondly, the highest concentration of casualties was sustained in that geo-political area, and thirdly, my research to date has focused mainly on the various nursing establishments based on the Western Front. In no way does this diminish the enormous contribution the men and nurses made to other geographical areas of military operations.

While writing the book, I was mindful of John Buchan's belief that 'the main features of the war can be more accurately seen and more truly judged by those who live through it than by a scholar writing after a lapse of half a century.' Consequently, I have simply sought to bring together the experiences of the men and women who, for four and a half years, fought, lived, loved and died together on the Western Front.

In recent years it has become fashionable for some historians to apply psychoanalytical theories to the words, deeds and motives of the men and women of that time. Unfortunately, some of these theories have been discredited or lack empirical evidence. There are, in addition, the ethical and moral problems associated with drawing conclusions about the conduct of human behaviour in warfare when some of the testaments come from men and women who may have been traumatised by their war experiences.

I have chosen to use the personal statements of the men and women who were involved in The Great War but I have refrained from placing my own interpretation on them; I believe it is up to readers to form their own opinions and draw their own conclusions from the testaments. Many of the statements in this book are anonymous and there are two reasons for this. Firstly, due to military censorship, nurses had to remain unidentified when they sent their dispatches back home as, quite often, these would have sent the military censor into a spin had they been discovered. But, with the aid of willing patients, letters tucked inside slings regularly dodged the censor. Secondly, in some parts of the text I have chosen, for ethical reasons and issues of sensitivity, not to name the men or women referred to. It is only ninety years since the Great War and the children and grandchildren of those men and women, I believe, have a right to family privacy.

The title, *It's a Long Way to Tipperary*, came about as a result of my own childhood experiences and personal associations with the song. I first heard 'Tipperary' when my grandmother played the tune for me on our beautiful Canadian maple piano. I loved the tune and I still do. Throughout the Great War, this song became one of the most popular and morale-raising pieces of music. It was sung on route marches, in billets, going in and out of the line, in estaminets, in hospitals and in rehabilitation and convalescing facilities. The emotion it evokes allows it to endure. My early introduction to the war time songs played and sung in my grandparents' home encouraged me to ask questions about the war and my family's role in it. Well-known war time song titles have been used as headings for chapters two to eight to reflect, not only the contents, but also the mood of the time.

I started life in my grandparents' home and the reality of my grandfather's war experiences was omnipresent. As a child, one of my favourite pastimes was looking at old photographs of cousins and uncles in military uniforms. My grandmother kept letters and postcards sent from the Front wrapped carefully inside an old green leather bag. I thought the lace and embroidered cards were beautiful. I still have them and the words on the cards have a great poignancy. I can look back now and understand why my grandmother so cherished these artefacts.

Caring for men of both World Wars during my early nursing career I marvelled at the Great War veterans with pieces of shrapnel embedded under their skin who would say, 'It's been there since ...' or 'the doctor said it couldn't be removed; it would kill me.' And yet, here they were, forty years later, admitted to hospital for the removal of their long-time irritations or the 'souvenirs of the war' as some men said of these offending pieces of metal. But it was not only their old shrapnel wounds that ailed them. In the Department of Respiratory Medicine, veterans were admitted with long-term chest conditions; annotations in the margins of their files would read, 'Gassed in the war.' It was also not uncommon in those days to read in patients' notes, 'War Neurosis', 'War Blinded' or 'War Amputee'. There is no doubt that my experiences of caring for the casualties of war have shaped my perception of war and how the human body and spirit can survive it.

Every day I pass a large gold framed photograph of one particular Great War veteran and casualty – my grandfather. Dressed in his army uniform, the photograph is a constant reminder of the war and the effect it had on my family, and millions like us. My grandfather was a Royal Irish Fusilier; he fought in the Easter Rising in Dublin and in the Battles of Guillemont and Ginchy on the Somme. As a consequence of his war service, my grandfather spent one year at King George V Military Hospital, Dublin, recovering from physical and psychological injuries. While in a rehabilitation hospital he met and fell in love with my grandmother. They were brought together at a hospital New Year's Eve concert where my grandmother entertained the wounded by playing their favourite songs on the piano; no doubt 'It's a Long Way to Tipperary' was one of them. Home was a long way from the killing grounds of France and Flanders and, when the guns eventually fell silent on 11 November 1918, the Nation, and the nursing profession, soon began to forget those nurses who did not return to their homes.

It is to the memory of the nurses, unsung warriors who unselfishly cared for the casualties of war, to my grandmother with her compassion, spirit and determination, and my grandfather and his comrades who gave and spent their all, that I dedicate this book.

## Chapter I

*Overtures and Undertones*

# Britain, Ireland and the Wider World 1901–1913

After sixty-four years as monarch, Queen Victoria died on 2 January, 1901. The Superintendent of Nursing in attendance recorded that the dying Queen had 'within a few minutes of death recognised the best beloved of her family' and that 'no death could have been more peaceful.' Nevertheless, as the nation mourned, it was suggested that professional nurses grieved more for their perceived loss of status than the death of their Queen. *The Nursing Record* placed the blame for this misconception on 'wide publicity by the lay press' which 'claimed that no professional nurses were in attendance on the Queen during her passing.'

Anxious to show 'its sorrow for the death of the Queen by some token of mourning,' the nursing leadership decided that 'a rosette of dull mourning ribbon, or crape, would be worn, and when indoors it would be pinned on the bib of the apron, on the left side, and when out doors, on the cloak … '.

This outward demonstration of mourning prompted *The Nursing Record* to reflect on the Queen's reign and ask what lesson could be learnt from the life of the dead Queen.

> It is noteworthy that women who have been entrusted with responsibility have rarely failed in the fulfilment of their trust, and the qualities of heart and mind so conspicuous in the Queen are those which in lesser degree have been characteristic also of her women subjects charged with public duties. Devotion to duty, a high sense of honour, truthfulness, tact, and sympathy, these are qualities which women bring to bear upon public affairs, and they are qualities which are needed in the public service. We are not slow to recognize the beneficent and world wide influence exerted by the Queen, and this influence was rooted in the characteristics she possessed by reason of her womanhood. The Queen's life has been an object lesson in woman's capacity, and the best gift of the nation in acknowledgment of the beneficence of her reign would be to remove the

disabilities under which British women suffer, and to give them the right to share in making laws they are required to keep. It can never again be urged, with the remembrance of Queen Victoria in the national heart, that public duties should be withheld from women on the grounds of their inability to discharge them.

The death of the Queen was an opportune moment to expose the flaws in arguments advanced by men that women should not enjoy parity of rights. The nursing journals supported the struggle for women's suffrage and linked it to their campaign for a Nurse Registration Bill. Over the coming years, nursing leaders would, at times, use significant national events quite shamelessly to promote professional recognition and to lobby for state registration.

Coronation year, 1902, and the beginning of the Edwardian era, was a good year for the nursing profession. Professional involvement in the South African War, and previous military campaigns, were acknowledged and rewarded by the formation of Queen Alexandra's Imperial Military Nursing Service. It had been a long struggle to have professionally trained nurses integrated into the Army Medical Services and it was as a direct consequence of the wholly inadequate medical and nursing arrangements during the three-year-long South African War that the reform of army nursing came about.

Apparently, the War Office had forgotten the lessons learned from the 1854–56 Crimean Campaign when medical arrangements and nursing provision were woefully inadequate. At that time, the Secretary of War, Sidney Herbert, expressed his concerns about the lack of professional nursing care for the sick and wounded, claiming, 'It will be difficult to find women equal to the task of nursing the sick and wounded after all the horrors of the situation are known.' In fact, women from a variety of social and religious backgrounds not only demonstrated they were 'equal to the task', but pioneered new and better ways of caring for the war-time sick and injured. The relative success of the involvement of nurses in the Crimean Campaign eventually led to a small cadre of professional nurses being posted with the British Army, and by the time the South African war broke out in 1899, professional nurses were involved in the Army's Medical Service, even though their potential contribution had not yet been recognised. Lord Roberts, who became Commander-in-Chief in 1901, was a keen supporter of the concept of military nurses and was asked by Queen Alexandra to submit his ideas on the development of the army nursing service. In a letter to the Queen on 4 February that year, he set out his thoughts.

Nursing in the Army is not altogether satisfactory, and the means by which it could be improved has long been a subject of anxious thought to me. If, however, Your Majesty will take the matter up, and give it Your

Royal name and support, I have little doubt but that an organisation could be devised which would be productive of good and important results. In the first place I think it would have the best possible effect if Your Majesty would consent to allow the Army Nursing Service to be called 'Queen Alexandra's Military Nursing Service for the United Kingdom, India and the Colonies.' I would suggest that, subject to Your Majesty's approval, a small committee of experienced ladies should be formed, who would work under Your Majesty as President, and discuss before laying them to you, Ma'am, the rules for, and the conditions, of the service. Some of the causes of the shortcomings of the present Nursing Service are:

A great number of the Nurses are too young which leads to their being somewhat frivolous, and also renders them more liable to fall victims to enteric, climate, etc.

Sufficient care has not been taken to get the opinions of the Matrons of hospitals where the nurses have been trained, as well as certificates from the Doctors as to their skill and general fitness. Sometimes the most attractive and not the most suitable for work in military hospitals have, I am afraid, been preferred. And finally a great number of the nurses are not of sufficiently good class.

There should be on the Committee an experienced nurse from one of the great London hospitals, for preference a lady who has gained experience during the war in South Africa ... You will therefore understand, Ma'am, the kind of nurse we think it would be desirable to have in Queen Alexandra's Military Nursing Service.

Two months later, Roberts wrote a letter to John Brodrick, the Secretary of State for War, enclosing a copy of the proposals he had submitted to the Queen:

There is no doubt improvement in the Nursing Service is needed, and in the Nurses being placed in a position to enable them to carry out their work in a proper manner. The Nurses are not as a rule in favour with Army Doctors, the good ones value them, but the others find they see too much of what is going on. Then again the relations between the Nurses and Orderlies are not satisfactory ... The Queen is pressing for the scheme.

Evidently, the Queen pressed hard enough; the Army Nursing Service was replaced by Queen Alexandra's Imperial Military Nursing Service, established by Royal Warrant on 27 March 1902. According to *The Nursing Record*:

For the first time in the history of a Government Nursing Department the value of expert professional help is thus officially recognised. We congratulate the Secretary of State for War that his Department has been the first to inaugurate this much needed reform.

When, on 9 August 1902, Edward VII was crowned King at Westminster Abbey, two professionally trained nurses were strategically placed in a discrete gallery behind the coronation chair. There were concerns about the King's health as, two months earlier, his appendix had been removed. The ceremony was shortened so that His Royal Highness did not exhaust himself by carrying the Sword of State. It was not the King, however, who required nursing skills but the Archbishop of Canterbury, who felt quite unwell and had to retire to Sir Edward's Chapel to collect himself. He later returned to conclude the service and, on behalf of the clerics of the Church of England, he swore allegiance to the new sovereign. Overcome by emotion or light-headedness, perhaps both, he had to be helped to his feet to conclude the proceedings. So, amidst the splendour, pomp and circumstance of fragile health, the era of the Edwardians was born.

Affectionately referred to as 'The Golden Age', it was a time of discovery, invention, daring, enterprise, earnest politics and political farce. It was the shock of the new and the death of conventionalism.

It was the era of ridiculously large hats, obscenely small waists, and harem skirts – an exotic euphemism for women's trousers. The struggle for women's emancipation was apparently reflected in the rise and fall of hems and necklines.

It was an era of great social and political reform and for some it was a time of frivolity and carefree behaviour. For the upper classes, dress and mood were based on the vagaries of the social calendar, or 'the season' as it was more pompously known.

It was a time when social inequalities were defined by ludicrous statements such as a claim made by one of the 'darling young things' of the debutante classes that 'it was impossible for a woman to do justice to herself on less than £1,000 per year.' Given that the average annual wage for women in domestic service ranged from £40–£50 for cooks, £18 for housemaids, £15 for kitchen-maids, and £8–£10 for young girls 'training' in domestic service, for the women of Edwardian Britain living on £50 a year and less, £1,000 could buy them a different type of 'justice'.

In Edwardian Britain, the prudery and conservatism of the Victorian Age were being eroded by the new dynamic of social and political liberalism. For women, particularly for those of the middle-class elite, the oppressiveness and social ethos that prevailed throughout Victoria's reign were to some extent altered in the new dawn of Liberalism. Education became more accessible for women and it became acceptable, if not commendable, for women to involve themselves in charitable or philanthropic work. In 19th century Britain, the rise of industrialisation, combined with a growing social conscience, had already brought significant opportunities for women of 'good religious and social standing' to carry out charitable works. At that time, Elizabeth Fry, famous for her work in penal reform, classically illustrates the mixture of religion, status and philanthropy of her time. Fry was born into a wealthy Quaker family; her father was a banker, as was her husband. Like other women from privileged backgrounds, she engaged with the need to reform the lives of the disadvantaged and dispossessed. Contrary to popular belief it was Elizabeth Fry, not Florence Nightingale, who, in early nineteenth-century Britain, founded the kernel of the nursing movement with the establishment of the Institution of Nursing Sisters.

By the time Edward VII was crowned King, nurses were involved in a variety of public health initiatives and hospital developments. But in spite of the approval of women's involvement in nursing, and charitable work, they were not allowed to vote, to hold public office, nor to stand for Parliament.

As early as 1792, Mary Wollstonecraft had been championing status issues for women and developed equality ideology in her book, *Vindication on the Rights of Women*. In 1832, Mary Smith, described as 'a lady of rank', petitioned Parliament, claiming that, under the law, there should be parity of franchise. Her petition claimed that as she paid taxes she should have a say in the election of political representatives, and further claimed that as women were liable to receive all the punishments of the law, not excluding death, they ought to have a voice in law-making.

Although there had been an ongoing campaign, increased activity and agitation by women lobbying for political and social inclusiveness, it was not until the Edwardian era that equality rights for women came to pre-eminence. The biggest force in campaigning for women's rights, although not subscribed to or approved of by all women, was the National Union of Women's Suffrage Societies (NUWSS), led by Millicent Garrett Fawcett. This organisation was a collective of local suffragist movements whose political agitation was carried out by means of law-abiding peaceful persuasion. The focus was on educating the public vis-à-vis women's rights and equality issues, mainly through pamphleteering and public speaking. Under the leadership of Emmeline Pankhurst, supported by her daughter Christabel, the militant wing of the women's suffrage movement was born – the Women's Social and Political Union (WSPU). They were known as suffragettes and they supported robust campaigning and aggressive tactics; if necessary, they were prepared to break the law in pursuit of their ideals.

The years 1902–1913 produced many new ideas. Innovation and invention were ripe, both nationally and internationally.

In science, the cause of malaria – the scourge of many military campaigns – was identified. The main ideas involved in Albert Einstein's important theories date back to this time, and the Wright brothers made their first successful flight in a petrol-powered aeroplane. Fingerprint evidence was used for the first time, and Alfred Binet invented the 'Intelligence Test'. Lieutenant-Colonel Henry Smith of the Indian Medical Service pioneered a new operation for cataracts. Madame Marie Curie became the first woman to win the Nobel Prize and Professor Ernest Rutherford of Manchester University became a Nobel Laureate for his research into the structure of the atom. The British Medical Association raised its concerns about the number of children smoking and chewing tobacco, one doctor claiming: 'Every boy and girl should be encouraged to sign a pledge never to take up the habit.'

In art and design, Charles Rennie Mackintosh came to represent and typify the Art Nouveau movement with his genius for architectural and interior design. Both he, and John Lavery, a son of Belfast who became a highly successful painter and was knighted in 1918, had studied at the Glasgow School of Art. Experimenting with the representation of the female form, Henri Matisse painted 'Le Luxe II', but more controversial was Pablo Picasso's 'Les Demoiselles d'Avignon', an interpretation of five nude women. The painting was widely attacked and Picasso was derided, not for his exposition of five nude women, but for his use of artistic licence in the composition of the bodies. Some people of his time even believed that it was his attempt at humour.

In literature, Sir Arthur Conan Doyle launched *The Hound of the Baskervilles*, Rudyard Kipling produced the *Just So Stories*, George Bernard Shaw introduced the world to *Man and Superman*, and Beatrix Potter gave birth to Peter Rabbit, metaphorically speaking, while D. H. Lawrence established his reputation as a writer with a semi-autobiographical novel, *Sons and Lovers,* which explored and examined attitudes towards sex and sexuality.

Internationally, after years of political posturing and dispute between Britain and France outstanding issues between the two countries were finally resolved, and the Entente Cordiale was born. In Russia the first of many pogroms against the Jews was carried out and in Serbia, the King and Queen were brutally murdered by a group of disaffected army officers who, after killing them, hacked them limb from limb.

The British Empire, according to the Government's Blue Book compiled by the English Local Government Board, occupied one-fifth of the global land surface and had a population of 400,000,000 'subjects'. The Aliens Act came into force and immigrants or refugees arriving in Britain were subjected to questions about their financial status and had to undergo physical and physiological tests; the Government seemed to prefer many of its 'subjects' to remain in their own part of the one-fifth!

In the United States of America, Congress sought to ban 'undesirables' from entering the country. The list of banned persons referred to 'anarchists, felons, polygamists, idiots, the insane and women of bad reputation' – some of the type of people who helped pioneer the country. The Ford Motor Company was formed, and the company's publicity material asserted in a very American, mother-and-apple-pie way, that 'All the World Loves a Ford, Even the Moon Beams'.

In Britain, the motor car became a feature of everyday life. For those with money, Charles Rolls and Henry Royce combined their respective talents and skills to establish quality motor vehicles. Their publicity posters claimed the Rolls Royce to be 'The Best Car in the World'. Perhaps they were interested in quality not quantity and did not cater for 'All the World, and Moon Beams'! The government introduced compulsory licence plates, but rejected the idea of imposing penalties for drink driving. Nevertheless, faced with the reality of drink driving accidents, London County Council established the first-ever motor ambulance service for the victims of road traffic accident.

Books of stamps went on sale for the first time, and postcards became popular. The new popular fad for postcards and the volumes being sent led the Postmaster-General to state that the country was in the grip of some form of mania. The largest number apparently was sent from Scotland though no explanation has been suggested for Scotland's obsession!

*The Nursing Times* was launched promising an 'unbiased' alternative to other nursing journals. The work and opinions of British and Irish nurses were already represented in the *Nursing Mirror*. Under the editorship of the highly opinionated and vocal Ethel Bedford Fenwick, the *British Journal of Nursing*, incorporating the *Nursing Record* continued to lobby for professional recognition and registration. Then, at the age of ninety-one, Florence Nightingale's lamp was extinguished; a memorial service was held at a packed St Paul's Cathedral, with floral tributes from royalty, matrons, nurses and branches of the army.

Liberal Governments introduced social legislation which by the standards of the time was radical. In matters of child welfare, The Education (Provision of Meals) 1906 Act and The Education (Administrative Provisions) Act 1907 allowed for the provision of school meals and the medical inspection of children at school. For the elderly, the Old Age Pensions Act 1908 guaranteed those over seventy years of age an annual income of between £21 and £31, and a pension of between one shilling (5p) and five shillings (25p) a week. The old age pension, however, was still two shillings (10p) short of what the entrepreneur and philanthropist Seebohm Rowntree considered to be the minimum necessary for the individual to live above the poverty line.

The sick were partly catered for by the The National Insurance Act Part I introduced in 1911, but not before it had been heavily contested by the British Medical Association which was more interested in securing the livelihood of its doctors than contributing to healthcare reform. Opposition also came from friendly societies and industrial insurance companies which considered their vested interests threatened by the legislation. Because of conflicting interests the final National Insurance scheme was a compromise.

Employment legislation introduced by the Liberal Government sought fundamental changes to improve working conditions. Under The Workmen's Compensation Act (1906) injury compensation was significantly improved. Employers in specified trades became liable to pay compensation to workers injured as a direct consequence of their working conditions or who had contracted industrial diseases. Under the new Act, cover was extended to nearly all employees. The Coal Mines Regulation Act (1908), or The Eight Hours Act as it was more commonly known, gave coal miners an eight-hour day for which they had campaigned for over forty years. The Trade Boards Act (1909) set up boards to negotiate minimum wages for the notoriously badly paid 'sweated trades'. A total of 200,000 workers were involved in trades such as tailoring, chain, box and lace making, and the majority of workers in those trades were women. The Shops Act (1911) entitled shop assistants to a weekly half-day off and a reasonable time allocated for meal breaks. The unemployed were assisted by the creation of The Labour Exchanges Act (1909) and The National Insurance Act Part II (1911) which allowed the unemployed to register for and find work. The Labour Exchanges also paid out benefits to the unemployed who were covered by insurance.

In Ireland, Ulster was preparing to mount challenges 'by any means' to attempted political reform proposed in the Home Rule Bill. In a dramatic demonstration of Ulster Protestant unity in Belfast in September 1912, 250,000 people signed the Solemn League and Covenant, the total signatories from Ulster amounting to 474,414. Its stated aim was 'to stand by one another in defending for ourselves and our children our cherished position of equal citizenship in the United Kingdom'. There was much Union Jack waving and, in a demonstration of a past remembered glory, James Craig MP produced a banner that allegedly had been carried at the Battle of the Boyne. A newspaper was later to comment: 'If that flag ever saw the Battle of the Boyne, all we can say is that the man who manufactured it deserves undying fame for the strength and durability of the material.' In the nationalist south, Pádraic Pearse stated that Ulster had just about got it right; its one mistake, he claimed, was its failure to identify the real enemy of the peoples of Ireland, suggesting, 'Why not unite and get rid of the English? They are the real difficulty.'

Apart from the 'Irish Question', George V, who was crowned on 22 June 1911 following the death of his father, Edward VII, on 6 May 1910, enjoyed three years of relative domestic peace and stability before his German cousin's advancing army darkened the horizon of Europe.

\*　\*　\*　\*

By 1913, Sir George Newman, Chief Medical Officer for Schools, had produced a report stating that 500,000 United Kingdom children were ill-fed and diseased. His survey had found that one in twelve children attending British state elementary schools were suffering from disease or the effects of poor diet. Of six million schoolchildren, more than half needed dental treatment and a third were 'unhygienically dirty'. One child in 10 had serious eye defects, nearly three in 100 had hearing problems or loss, two in 100 had heart disease and one in 100 had tuberculosis. Furthermore, one child in 100 had ringworm and one in ten required surgery for inflamed tonsils. It was a depressing report but just one of many reporting on the causal links between poverty and ill health, and the miseries and tragedies that the 'economic disease' had on individuals or communities.

The suffragettes continued their campaigns against Asquith's Liberal Government with more social disruption, violence and hunger strikes. Almost daily, the unsympathetic press carried stories about their 'unfeminine activities' or lampooned them in a series of cartoons, such as 'This is the House that Man Built' (The Palace of Westminster). In one cartoon, a caricature of a spinster was depicted standing on a stool looking terrified at a mouse below. The caption read:

> This is the House that Man Built
> The House that our Statesmen for years have controlled
> Ruling the world with minds fearless and bold!
> Can women expect to rule such a house?
> She that's afraid of a poor little mouse
> No! No!! Suffragette your place is not yet,
> Inside the House that Man Built.

In order to deal with the problem of suffragettes going on hunger strike while serving their prison sentences, the Government drafted 'The Cat and Mouse Bill' which enabled the Home Secretary to release the women from jail until they had recovered from the health effects of their fast; they were re-arrested when they were fit to continue their sentence. Exasperated by the Government's actions, Emily Davison, a suffragette who had been imprisoned and force-fed on several occasions, threw herself under the King's horse on Derby Day. Miss Davison, an English graduate, was later to die in hospital of wound complications. *The Times*, reporting the death, further informed readers that:

A number of lady friends called at the Epsom Cottage Hospital on Saturday afternoon to inquire as to the condition of Miss Davison. Two visitors draped the screen round the bed with the WSPU colours and tied them to the head of the bed.

Writing in *The Times* twelve days after the Davison tragedy, the writer and satirist George Bernard Shaw summed up the political farce into which the franchise debate had descended.

Mr Asquith for the first time opposed the franchise for women on the ground that woman is not the female of the human species, but a distinct and inferior species, naturally disqualified from voting as a rabbit is disqualified from voting. A man may object to the proposed extension of the suffrage for many reasons. He may hold that the whole business of popular election is a delusion, and that votes for women is its reduction to absurdity. He may object to it as upsetting convenient divisions of labour between the sexes. He may object to it because he dislikes change, or is interested in businesses, or practices which women would use political power to suppress. But it is one thing to follow a Prime Minister who advances all, or some, or any of these reasons for standing in the way of votes for women. It is quite another to follow a Prime Minister who places one's mother on the footing of a rabbit.

Whilst suffragettes throughout Britain were in the midst of an important political struggle to be taken seriously, the extent of the pursuit of knowledge by some psychiatrists with regard to behavioural science amounted to a study of 'why women enjoyed dressing up'. Dr C. T. Ewart, a London 'nerve' specialist, carried out 'research' and identified two distinct types of women who experienced 'an emotional accompaniment of elation following the putting on of attractive garments'. For the sake of scientific integrity and unbiased research, the study perhaps could have examined the 'elation' factor, as it applied to men who donned women's clothes in pantomime and music halls! While psychiatrists wrestled with the female psyche, the new Mental Deficiency Act defined four classes of defectives: idiots, imbeciles, feeble-minded and moral defectives; it did not mention women (or men) who liked dressing up.

Sex and contraception were discussed in pamphlets such as, 'What Women ought to know on the Subject of Sex'. Cartoon postcards played their part in sex education. Reminding couples of the need to practise safe sex, one postcard illustrated a male and female sitting coyly beside each other, with a caption stating, 'Be good. If you can't be good be careful.' From the days when it was claimed that 'girls from a respectable family shouldn't look at newspapers,' or that 'women appearing in Regent Street after 10 o'clock in the evening, must expect to be molested', female liberty and sexuality were moving on apace!

Road accident statistics were now being compiled and the number of licensed motor vehicles was approximately 100,000. There were 1,070 fatal road accidents and 26,091 non-fatal; this figure did not include bicycle accidents. It was reported that, since 1907, street deaths involving motor buses had risen five-fold. It was recommended that in busy areas speed limits required greater attention; the limit at Hyde Park Corner was then 10 mph. While road deaths gave the public and authorities cause for concern, heavy industry was producing high fatality rates. In 1913, mining alone saw 1,753 miners killed in pit accidents and 178,962 suffered injuries that required absence from work for more than seven days. In the autumn of that year there was a tragic mining disaster at the Senghenydd Colliery, Glamorganshire, when 440 miners were killed in an underground explosion. The cause of the disaster was firedamp ignited by sparks from an electrical signalling device. Some families lost more than one member and the deaths affected nearly every household in the community. The coming conflict in Europe would see 230,000 miners volunteer for war service with similar consequences.

As the year ended and the pine needles fell from dying Christmas trees, the nursing press covered the activities of Christmastide in British and Irish hospitals. At Salford Royal Hospital, the Mayor and Mayoress 'dispensed hospitality to the guests who came to watch the distribution of toys and gifts to the sick and injured'. The Matron and nurses at St Mary's Hospital, London, held a children's Christmas tree party, 'leaving nothing undone to ensure the comfort of the guests and the happiness of their carefully tended small charges'. Dagenham's Sanatorium for the Treatment of Tuberculosis was decorated with 'effective and pleasing designs and strings of gay paper, and evergreens were pinned to the wall'. Hanging in the centre of the recreation room was a large teddy bear labelled 'The TB we prefer'. It was noted that every patient received a present by 'dipping into the Lucky Tub' and, according to the report, 'there was much music and singing and a thoroughly happy and enjoyable Christmas Day was brought to a close with hearty cheers and the singing of the National Anthem.'

In Scotland, with practicality being a characteristic of the nation, the annual Christmas gathering at the Western Infirmary, Glasgow, was seen as the ideal time to acknowledge the medical and nursing staff's contribution to their respective vocations. The congratulations fell to Dr Mackintosh for his 'twenty-one years of service as the Medical Superintendent of the hospital'. The Nursing Superintendent, Miss Gregory-Smith, was acknowledged for 'all she had done for the development of the hospital, and the improvement of it as a training school for nurses'.

Edinburgh nurses were less Presbyterian in their Christmas celebrations. In the recreational hall of the City Fever Hospital, an exhibition of Old English folk dances was given and members of the nursing profession were advised to 'study these fine old dances as an ideal form of recreation, possessing great value, not only as physical exercise, but also from an artistic and educative standpoint'. The dancing demonstration closed with a 'delightful tea' supplied by the Matron.

In Ireland, the festivities were livelier. At Mercer's Hospital, Dublin, the Matron and medical staff were 'At Home' to the numerous friends and governors of the hospital. An 'extremely good concert' was held in one of the larger wards, where all the patients who were able to be moved were assembled. The nursing staff produced a concert that consisted of 'a most amusing Umbrella Dialogue presented by nurses O'Rourke and Williams', 'nurses Clarke and O'Driscoll, dressed in green and scarlet, dancing an Irish jig, accompanied by the piano playing of nurse Roche', a comical sketch entitled, 'The Rich Aunt from California' was cleverly rendered, and 'Sister MacArdle especially brought the house down by her amusing acting in the part of Aunt Sallie.'

The Rotunda Hospital, Dublin, was 'beautifully decorated by the sisters and nursing staff' and there were carol concerts throughout the wards. The corridors of the hospital were dressed in greenery with Japanese lanterns hanging criss-cross along the ceiling and fairly lights lined all the window ledges. The wards were decorated with holly and ivy and there were large quantities of flowers on the ward tables and chimney shelves.

The popular press reported that the musical hits of 1913 were, 'You made me love you', 'Hello! Hello! Who's your lady friend?' and 'He'd have to get under, get out and get under'.

On the last day of 1913 elaborate programmes of celebrations were staged for seeing in the New Year. At the Waldorf Hotel, London, tables were decorated with miniature dirigible airships; printed on one side was 'The Waldorf Hotel' and on the other '1913'. They were released and sailed away into space as the lights went out at the stroke of twelve. When the lights were turned on, an enormous pie embellished with swans, pheasants and *mangel wurzels* was carried in on the shoulders of four men. From the middle of the pie a lady appeared, singing 'Auld Lang Syne' and hundreds of crackers filling the pie were distributed.

At Prince's Hotel and Restaurant in London, tango exhibitions were given in the rose-decorated ballroom. The tango had become the latest dance craze but it was described by its detractors as 'suggestive and indecent'. One member of the clergy, clearly not a dance fan, described the tango as 'one of those animal dances that have no raison d'être but to gratify animal passions'.

In Germany also, the tango was proving to be a very popular dance, so much so that the Kaiser expressed his disfavour and issued an order requesting his army and navy not to dance the tango or the two-step; failure to respect his request would result in dismissal.

At the London Piccadilly Club, according to press reports, the prevailing colour in the New Year table decorations was soft pink, and the menu was 'a most artistic piece of work', while the 'Welcome 1914' in the lights of many colours was most effective.'

As the coloured lights went out on the Christmastide of 1913, three nurses – Evelyn Luard, a forty-four year old vicar's daughter from the sleepy hollow of Birch in Essex, recently posted to a military hospital in Dublin, Catherine Black, a thirty-two year old draper's daughter from the rugged beauty of County Donegal in Ireland, now working in London, and Millicent Bruce Peterkin, a twenty-six year old solicitor's daughter from Edinburgh, nursing at the Royal Infirmary and a member of the well-known Usher brewing dynasty – would remember this season along with their colleagues and countless families in Britain and Ireland, not for its beautiful, comical and elaborate festivities but as the last Christmas for many years without the presence and memory of the disfigured, diseased, distressed, dying and dead casualties of war.

Chapter II

## *'Oh! We don't want to lose you but we think you ought to go'*

# Dissent and Disaster 1914

Professional nurses believed that the Liberal Government's employment and welfare reforms had not gone far enough. Professional registration was an important matter still to be tackled. Since 1905, nurses had continuously lobbied for a Register of Trained Nurses to regulate the qualifications of nurses and to provide for state-sanctioned registration. As it was, the whole system of nurse practice and training left the public, including nurses themselves, in a state of confusion. There was no easy way to distinguish between the training, quality and calibre of women who claimed to be nurses. Arguing that there was no valid reason for further delays to the implementation of the Registration Bill, nurses asserted they had contributed, and were continuing to contribute, significantly to the health of the nation. Citing their involvement in past military campaigns and public health development at home, nurses claimed they had more than demonstrated their worth to society.

Nursing journals of the time leave no doubt about the range of issues with which nurses were involved. In early 1914, *The Nursing Times* reported on a new treatment for obesity. The 'cure' came in the form of the Bergonie System, a Faradic battery with electrodes, which stimulated the muscles when attached to the body. Its purpose was to 'increase the vitality of organs through intermittent contractions of the muscles aimed at fulfilling the same effect as that produced by proper exercise.' It was claimed this led to 'dramatic weight loss'. The small print, however, stated that 'the patient must necessarily be dieted according to individual needs, and in most cases vegetables only are ordered.' This gadget was frippery for fools, as the 'cure' was clearly in the vegetable diet. *The Nursing Times* also examined the variety of psychotherapeutic treatments available for patients with 'nervous disorders', such as hypnotism, psycho-analysis, psycho-electric therapy, and persuasion and it suggested that it would be 'wrong' to encourage nurses to 'make use of the highly technical processes, nevertheless, with increased knowledge of the subject, more good can be done than by simple, haphazard application of half-appreciated facts.' According to the journal, Scotland was taking the lead in the treatment of mental health problems. In the country's Poor Law Hospitals, there were observation wards, their purpose supposedly being the prevention of insanity. The journal supported the Scottish system, claiming that hospital treatment should be made available 'where, without any stigma of insanity' patients could easily go for advice and care 'in the early stages of mental instability, so that a certain proportion never become certifiable'. It went further claiming that 'The Scottish system in this respect, as in other social matters is advanced.' *The Nursing Times* also covered the Nursing and Midwifery Conference and Exhibition held in Glasgow and encouraged nurses to come forward with any of their own 'inventions, devices and ideas' which could contribute to patient care and comfort. Prizes of Gold, Silver and Bronze Medals, in addition to £8, £2 and £1 cash rewards, were offered for their inventions.

Another nursing journal, the *British Journal of Nursing*, also reported on current medical issues such as the novel idea that there was a causal link between cancer and cigarette smoking. Research carried out over a two-year period by the Medical Officer of Health for Woolwich concluded there was some evidence to support the theory that cigarettes were harmful to health. The significance of nursing practice and penal reforms was highlighted when the journal published a paper on 'Nursing in Prisons' given in June 1914 at the Birmingham Nurses Conference by Mrs Maxwell, a trained nurse. Addressing her colleagues Mrs Maxwell asked:

> How, I ask you, can we nurses contemplate the prison system without wishing to alter it? I must confess that my chief motive in advocating the introduction of trained nurses into prisons is the hope that they will help to transform them out of recognition ... Discussing these matters one day with a doctor, I urged the desirability of having trained nurses of culture in all prisons. 'He looked shocked, and said that prison was not a place for ladies. I think the answer to that is that the sooner prison becomes a place for ladies the better ... I seriously ask my sister nurses if they do not feel that prison is eminently a place for us?

In July, the *British Journal of Nursing* gave considerable space to a paper by Mrs Mabel St Clair Stobart which she had presented at the Nursing and Midwifery Conference held in London. The main contention was the lack of professional organisation and aid given to the sick and wounded in war time. Mrs Stobart, a veteran nurse of the 1912–1913 Balkan Wars, had created the British Women's Convoy Corps, a medical unit staffed by women serving in the front line. Criticising the all-male composition of the Executive

Committee of the British Red Cross Society, she claimed: 'There are twelve men, and there is not one woman.' The Voluntary Aid Advisory Sub-Committee appointed by the Executive Committee had 'a few ladies, representative of the aristocracy of various counties of England and Wales, but there is not one representative of the nursing profession.' Mrs St Clair Stobart was trying to use these insightful and timely observations to ensure that 'those women who only seek drawing-room amusement' could never secure positions of responsibility in the management and care of war casualties.

Important though these issues were, the burning professional issue for nurses was not public health, prison reform or war but the debacle over State Registration. In an editorial, the *British Journal of Nursing* expressed exasperation about the time it was taking to secure the passing of the Bill, declaring:

> The Nurses Registration Bill has been before the House of Commons for the past ten years, read for the first time, and then because the antiquated procedures of the People's House, permits one man to thwart the people's will, it has never had a second reading ... In our opinion it is the clear duty of the Government to grant this petition. A Liberal Government cannot consistently, with Liberal principles, allow a few members to stultify reform which both Houses of Parliament have clearly demonstrated is, in their opinion, necessary.

Some forty years earlier the medical journal, *The Lancet*, claimed that nurses 'possess just enough knowledge to make them dangerous'. Since then there had been little acknowledgement and recognition of their continued professional development and skills. In the summer of 1914, Dr Chapple MP presented a petition to the Prime Minister on behalf of the Central Committee for the State Registration of Nurses; 525 matrons and superintendents from England, Scotland and Ireland signed the document. This was not enough, however, to change the attitude of the Government which did not consider nursing to be a profession or worthy of State Registration. The politics of The Nurses Registration Bill was not of paramount concern to Asquith's Government; it was far more troubled by the Suffragettes.

The militancy of the Women's Social and Political Union (WSPU) paled in comparison to the threat of a general strike as proposed by the 'Triple Alliance' of miners, transport workers and railwaymen who were planning to bring the country to a standstill if their demands for a minimum wage were not met.

Even more disturbing than either the threat of suffragette violence or a national industrial dispute was the potentially explosive effect the implementation of the Government's Home Rule Bill for Ireland could have on Ireland and Britain. This bill had been through a long and tortuous process, with significant political fall-out and ramifications during its evolution. Under the leadership of John Redmond and his Irish Parliamentary Party, Irish Nationalism finally had gained constitutional recognition from the Liberal Government. For some Irish Nationalists the third and final reading of the Government of Ireland Bill on 25 May 1914 was crucial. Under the terms of the Bill, Ireland would have its own domestic affairs legislature while Parliament in London would focus on foreign policy, taxation, the armed forces and issues relating to war and peace. In predominantly Protestant Ulster, Sir Edward Carson, the leader of the Ulster Unionists, was bitterly opposed to the idea. For Ulster Protestants, the ideology of Home Rule was synonymous with 'Rome Rule'. Three years earlier, James Craig, the Unionist MP for East Down, had invited Sir Edward Carson to open the campaign against the Home Rule Bill. Addressing a crowd of 50,000 men from Orange Lodges and Unionist Clubs in Ulster, Carson proclaimed:

> I know the responsibility you are putting on me today. In your presence I cheerfully accept it, grave as it is. We must be prepared the morning Home Rule passes, ourselves to become responsible for the government of the Protestant Province of Ulster.

By autumn 1912, Ulster was convulsed with anti-home rule meetings, culminating on 28 September with the signing of a 'Solemn League and Covenant' by those loyal to 'their cherished position of equal citizenship in the United Kingdom'. The total number of signatures was 471,414, many men signing the covenant in their own blood. Loyalist women signed a separate declaration.

By January 1913, Carson, in an amendment to the Home Rule Bill, wanted Ulster excluded. Simultaneous to his opposition to the Bill, a private army, the Ulster Volunteer Force (UVF), was formed. The idea for its formation was first suggested in 1886 by Colonel Saunderson, the leader of the Ulster Unionists and the Orange Order, who felt planned military resistance to Home Rule was necessary. The UVF, organised on a quasi-military basis, had a complement of 90,000 personnel and all the support systems of a regular army, such as signals, medical, catering and transport. The emergence of the UVF prompted a similar response from Nationalist Ireland in the form of the Irish National Volunteers, inaugurated in November 1913, and committed to oppose, by force, any attempt by Unionists and the UVF to destroy the implementation of the Home Rule Bill. They claimed their objective was 'to secure and maintain the rights and liberties common to all the people of Ireland'. In a somewhat precarious coalition, a broad spectrum of support came from the Home Rule Movement, members of the Irish Republican Brotherhood (IRB), academics, trade unionists and followers of

John Redmond's Irish National Party. The men of the south were determined to subvert what they perceived to be the tyrannical political will imposed on them by the Ulster Unionists.

By 1914, Ireland had two unofficial citizen armies, both prepared to fight each other in support of, and against, Home Rule. Concerns about a civil war were real, and fear was omnipresent. The situation was serious enough to warrant advertisements and letters being placed in nursing journals requesting trained nurses to volunteer their services should a conflict erupt in Ireland. On 25 July *The Nursing Times* published the following:

TRAINED NURSES FOR IRELAND

We learn that a large number of nurses (fifty-five 'trained' and thirty 'semi-trained' up to July 10th, and many more since) have responded to the invitation of the Ulster Hospital Corps, advertised in *THE NURSING TIMES* and other journals, but that there is urgent need for more. No payment is offered except for passages in case of need, but hospitality is provided. The special need is for fully trained nurses able to take charge of small stationary hospitals and dressing stations.

We learnt in an interview with one of the staff that by 'semi-trained' is meant nurses who are still in the probationary stage of their training, and that a few volunteers with St. John Ambulance or Red Cross certificates have also been accepted. The demand, however, is for fully trained nurses, and volunteers are asked to allow their certificates to be inspected at the headquarters, 112 Beaufort Street, Chelsea. Both Irish and English [British] nurses are showing their patriotic spirit by volunteering, and among them are some who served in the South African War. A large number of the volunteers are in private work, and they are, of course, taking the risk of losing cases, and therefore part of their income. The Corps is under the Presidency of Lord Aldenham, and Lord Roberts is a member of the Committee.

We should like to suggest that if, in addition, the Committee included the names of one or two matrons or nurses well known in the hospital world, nurses would be likely to feel greater confidence in sending in their names for this truly patriotic work. The Corps works in close connection with the Ulster Medical Board, and nurses will be sent to any part of Ireland where they may be wanted. The Corps has, of course, no political bias, and is simply being raised to nurse the wounded in case of fighting in Ireland.

On the same day the letter below appeared in the *British Journal of Nursing:*

Madam,

We are in great need of more trained nurses to work in Ireland in case of trouble. We are offering no payment, but will pay passages for those who cannot afford their own, and Ulster is offering board and lodging. We particularly want nurses who can take charge of small hospitals and dressing stations. Precautions are taken against a panic mobilisation, as many of our Volunteers would be giving up posts in order to go. We have no expenses at present beyond stationery and postages, as the office is lent and the staff is voluntary. Large amounts of medical and surgical stores have been ordered provisionally to be delivered at twelve hours' notice if required.

KATHARINE FURSE
Ulster Hospital Corps
112, Beaufort Street
Chelsea, S.W.

In Ulster, preparations for civil war were well underway. Between 24 and 25 April, attempts at gun-running were successful when 35,000 rifles and three million rounds of ammunition were landed at the east-coast ports of Larne, Donaghadee and Bangor. The well-planned nocturnal operations were carried out with military precision and the arms were successfully distributed throughout Ulster by thousands of men.

In an act of political opportunism, Mrs Pankhurst and representatives from the WSPU asked Sir Edward Carson if Ulster were to have its own government, would it give equal voting rights to women. According to Emmeline Pankhurst, Carson had at one time promised that, should an Ulster Government come into existence, Ulster women would receive the franchise. Mrs Pankhurst's question was ignored and the franchise claim repudiated. Consequently, Ulster suffragettes, reminding everyone that the WSPU was still a force to be reckoned with, embarked on a campaign of militancy. On 14 July *The Belfast Newsletter* reported:

Beautiful Mansion near Belfast Gutted
Damage Estimated at £20,000

Ballymenoch House, one of the largest and most stately mansions in Ulster, was totally gutted by fire yesterday. Between five and six o'clock yesterday morning it was discovered that the building was on fire.

Although the brigade remained on the scene until half-past three yesterday afternoon, they were unable to do any effective work after the water supply failed, and when they left the whole of the roof collapsed. About four o'clock, when the fire seemed to have spent itself, huge sheets of flame commenced to shoot up from the cellars, and burnt fiercely until everything of a combustible nature had been destroyed.

No explanation can be given for the origin of the fire, but two copies of the 'Suffragette', the organ of the militant women, were found in the grounds, and on the windows of the conservatory, which are painted white, the words 'Votes for Women' had been written.

Three months after the illegal importation of arms in the north, an attempt at gun running by Irish Volunteers in the south was less successful, culminating in death and bloodshed. On Sunday 26 July 2,500 Lee-Enfield rifles and 125,000 rounds of ammunition were landed at Howth, near Dublin. Approximately 1,000 Irish Volunteers unloaded the cargo. Each man shouldered a rifle and the rest of the armaments were transported by motor vehicles to various pre-arranged destinations throughout the countryside. It was claimed that, following the unloading of the shipment, the volunteers 'formed up and, in an orderly and well controlled manner, marched on to Dublin'. The Irish Volunteers were met by members of the Dublin Metropolitan Police Force who were later assisted by soldiers from a Scottish Regiment, the King's Own Scottish Borderers. According to the official report, 'while parleying was going on between the authorities and the front ranks of the Volunteers, the rest of the volunteers, with the arms, completely disappeared.' The incident apparently ended with no more than a scuffle between the parties although it was alleged that some bayonet wounds had been inflicted.

Later in the day, when the soldiers were attempting to return to their barracks, the incident spilled over to Bachelors Walk in Dublin. A crowd followed the soldiers and tried to provoke them with jibes and jeering. Verbal assaults were followed by physical force; bottles, stones and other missiles were thrown at the troops. In a sequence of confusion and misunderstandings about the orders to respond, the soldiers fired into the crowd. Lives were lost, and many sustained serious injuries. A nurse at Jervis Street Hospital in Dublin described the civilian injuries:

> There were sixteen patients there, all with wounds as on the field of battle. I was shown the radiographs prepared by Dr Maurice Hayes, which showed the presence of bullets, pellets and shot, so the ammunition was very varied. One small boy only ten years old had a bullet embedded in his liver, another man they fear will have to have both legs amputated. I saw two girls, who must both have been shot when running from the soldiers, as the bullets (not yet extracted) were in the calves of their legs, one having a bullet in her thigh as well as one in each of her legs. I spoke to them and found they were mostly innocent victims, who got caught in the crowd. As a great many of the nurses were away on their holidays, the staff of private nurses attached to the hospital had to be requisitioned for duty. These extra cases make the wards very busy and full, but the nurses seem very bright and cheerful. They are having quite a new experience in gunshot wounds. Afterwards I visited the scene of carnage, and saw large

blood splashes on the walls; each place where the three poor people lost their lives is marked by crosses made with white chalk. The Dublin papers speak highly of the work done by the sisters and nurses. Three cases were also treated at the Mater Misericordiae Hospital.

**The Doherty family in 1914. The father and three sons (one of them, Patrick, was the author's grandfather) would soon be fighting in France.**

While the threat of domestic conflict was preoccupying the Liberal Government and nurses, the Archduke Franz Ferdinand and his wife were assassinated on 28 June in Sarajevo, the provincial capital of Bosnia. The Archduke was Heir-Presumptive to the Habsburg Monarchy, controlling the Austro-Hungarian Empire. Bosnia and its sister province, Hercegovina, had been administered by the Habsburgs. The political situation bred resentment amongst the local population, many of whom, and especially Serbs, longed for a union with the neighbouring, independent, state of Serbia.

Following the assassinations – carried out by Gavrilo Princip, a Serbian Nationalist – Austria-Hungary, backed by Germany, presented a humiliating ultimatum to Serbia. Serbia accepted almost all of its demands, knowing that it was in no position to fight another war – even one with the promise of Russian support.

For over a month, political brinkmanship was played out by the main protagonists. France stood ready to assist Russia if threatened by Germany, and vice versa. Britain would assist France if the vital interests of both were under threat. France clearly saw the situation as an opportunity to win back the territories of Alsace and Lorraine, lost to Germany during the 1870–1871 Franco-Prussian war. It was the threat of a German invasion into neutral Belgium that finally ignited the political tinderbox. In order to secure a swift victory against France, Germany needed to advance her army through Belgium. The neutrality of Belgium had been guaranteed by the 1831 Treaty of London, signed by Great Britain, France, Austria, Russia and Prussia. The German Chancellor, Bethmann von Hollweg, was later to comment, 'Just for a scrap of paper Great Britain was going to make war on a kindred nation who desired nothing better than to be friends with her.' Britain was determined to respect both the letter and spirit of the agreement.

Ironically, King George V, Kaiser Wilhelm II and Tsar Nicolas II were all first cousins. In spite of the personal communiqués between the cousins throughout the crisis, forces greater than family ties were at work. The heady mixture of national pride, military, political and commercial ambitions, ultimatums and premature mobilisation, made a war in Europe inevitable. The people of Britain and Ireland had no sense of commitment to such a war. Britain had not been involved in a European war since the days of Napoleon I and the power struggles and tensions within the great European nations were no greater than in previous years. Yet the expansion of the German Navy aroused concern. Winston Churchill, First Lord of the Admiralty in 1914, was later to write, 'All sorts of sober-minded people began to be profoundly disquieted. What did Germany want this great navy for?' Nevertheless, Britain did not seek conflict and was more interested in maintaining and developing the vast empire she had acquired; as the greatest creditor nation in the world, she had lent £4,000,000,000 to other countries and as the greatest manufacturing country in Europe, her financial security was enviable.

A Cabinet meeting of the British Government held on 24 July, concluded that conflict seemed inevitable between the four continental powers but Britain need not be dragged into the 'Balkan quarrel'. Churchill claimed it was at this meeting, originally convened to discuss the worsening Irish situation, that ministers were first made aware of the declining situation in Europe and the significance of events there. Sir Edward Gray, the Foreign Secretary, read out a document just received from the Foreign Office which outlined ultimata being issued in Europe. Churchill recalled, 'The parishes of Fermanagh and Tyrone faded back into the mist and squalls of Ireland, and a strange light began to fall and grow upon the map of Europe.'

The 'Balkan Quarrel' was beginning to capture the interest, if not the imagination, of newspapers. On 29 July, the *Daily News* claimed: 'Not a British life will be sacrificed for the sake of a Russian hegemony of the Slav world.' The following day, the paper had even stronger words for politicians and the readership: 'We must not have our Western civilisation submerged in a sea of blood in order to wash out a Serbian conspiracy.'

By Sunday, 1 August, Britain was still hoping that diplomacy would avert a 'sea of blood' in Europe. On 2 August, Germany delivered its final ultimatum to Belgium, threatening military action against her if she did not grant the use of her territory in Germany's operations against France. As 600,000 German troops mobilised towards the French and Luxembourg frontiers, the threat became a reality. On Tuesday, 4 August, King Albert of Belgium sent a telegram to King George: 'I make a supreme appeal to the diplomatic intervention of your Majesty's Government to safeguard the integrity of Belgium.' Britain sent an ultimatum to Germany, demanding the termination of military action against neutral Belgium.

On the advent of the inevitable, the *Daily News*, which had been so adamant that Britain should not be embroiled in a European war, had to concede: 'Let us fight, if we must, without bitterness and without malice, so that when the tragedy is over we may make an honourable peace.'

On the eve of the declaration of war, the Parliamentary correspondent of *The Times*, Michael MacDonagh, described the almost carnivalesque scenes in and around Whitehall.

Parliament Street and Whitehall were thronged with people highly excited and rather boisterous ... all were already touched with war fever. They regarded their country as a crusader – redressing all wrongs and bringing freedom to oppressed nations. Cries of 'Down with Germany' were raised. Germany was the aggressor ... There were opponents, of course. Making my way through the crowds to Trafalgar Square, I found two rival demonstrations in progress under Nelson's Pillar – on one side of the plinth for war, and on the other against! The rival crowds glared at each other. Cries of 'The War does not concern us; we must keep out of it', were answered with cries of 'Down with Germany, the violator of Belgium ...

At Buckingham Palace the crowd sang 'God Save the King' with tremendous fervour. His Majesty came out on to the balcony overlooking the forecourt, wearing the uniform of Admiral of the Fleet. He was joined by the Queen, the Prince of Wales and Princess Mary. The crowd greeted the King by singing, with cheerful boisterousness, that homely British song, 'For He's a Jolly Good Fellow'.

At the approach of the decisive hour of eleven (midnight German time) when the ultimatum to Germany was to expire, we returned in our thousands to Whitehall. Downing Street was as packed as it well could be. At No. 10, the Prime Minister's house, were gathered leading members of the Government. While we waited, there was an incessant coming and going of callers but no answer had come from Germany.

When Big Ben struck eleven on 4 August 1914, Britain was at war. MacDonagh described the final minutes:

> Then followed the slow and measured strokes of Big Ben proclaiming to London that it was eleven o'clock. Was he booming out the true and in the false? Was he booming out sweet peace and in red slaughter?
> At the eleventh stroke of the clock, the crowd, swarming in Downing Street, Parliament Street and Parliament Square, burst with one accord into 'God Save the King' ... No one came out of 10 Downing Street. No statement was made. There was no public proclamation that we were at war by a herald to the sound of trumpets and the beating of drums. The great crowd rapidly dispersed in all directions, most of them running to get home quickly, and as they ran they cried aloud rather hysterically, 'War, War, War'.

Sitting in the War Room of the Admiralty, Winston Churchill recalled:

> From Parliament Street came the murmurs of the crowd; but they sounded distant and the world seemed very still. The tumult of the struggle for life was over; it was succeeded by the silence of ruin and death. We were to awake in pandemonium.

Margot Asquith, wife of the Prime Minister, described the last few hours of anguish for her husband and herself when it appeared that war with Germany was inevitable.

> 'So it is all up?' I said. He answered without looking at me, 'Yes, it's all up.' I sat down beside him ... Henry sat at his writing table leaning back with a pen in his hand ... What was he thinking of? ... His sons? ... My son was too young to fight; would they all have to fight ... I got up and leant my head against his: we could not speak for tears ... How did it ... how could it have happened? What were we all like five days ago? We were talking about Ireland and Civil War; Civil War! People were angry but not serious: and now the sound of real war waved like wireless round our heads and the whole world was listening.

In Berlin, on the eve of war, the *Daily News* journalist, H. W. Nevinson, felt, as a foreigner, extremely vulnerable.

> In the Reichstag, the Chancellor, Bethmann Hollweg, announced that, under the plea of necessity, the neutrality of Belgium had almost certainly already been violated. Then I knew that the long-dreaded moment had come ... While I was dining I heard the yells of a crowd shouting outside our Embassy in the neighbouring street and breaking the windows with

loud crashes. Soon the noise came nearer and, in front of the hotel entrance, I could distinguish shouts for the English correspondents to be brought out.

The wild outcries were chiefly directed against a prominent American correspondent who, in support of his London paper's policy, had been sending messages far from conciliatory. He and my colleague, who was acting with me for the *Daily News*, were given up to the police by the hotel director and, as I was passing into the front hall to see what was happening, he pointed me out as well. Two of the armed police seized me at once and dragged me out, holding an enormous revolver at each ear. If you try to run away, they kept shouting, we will shoot you like a dog! During this conversation they flung me out into the mob, who savagely set upon me with sticks, fists, and umbrellas ... The police then took me, with a Dutch correspondent, by taxi to the Praesidium, or central police court; there our treatment became more courteous, and after we had made our statements and shown our passports we were dismissed, with a note insuring protection ... So, imitating to myself the saying of the herald who proclaimed the beginning of the long war between Athens and Sparta 'This day sees the beginning of many sorrows for the most civilised peoples of the world ... '

According to *The Times*, 'A quiet group of matrons of the nursing service spent the Sunday before the declaration of war waiting in the electric atmosphere of the War Office for news that meant so much for them as well as for the army.' At the outbreak of war there were three branches of the military nursing service. Of the three, The Queen Alexandra's Imperial Military Nursing Service (QAIMNS) was a full-time senior service. The QAIMNS Reserve was formed in 1908 to supplement the work of the full-time Nursing Service in the event of war. The third component, the Territorial Force Nursing Service (TFNS), was inaugurated in 1908 and had 3,000 reserve nurses. The function of the TFNS was primarily to serve around the country in the twenty-three designated Territorial Hospitals (TH), controlled by the War Office and under Army administration. At the outbreak of war, each TH had 520 beds, a nursing service of ninety-one and a reserve of thirty. In addition to the military nursing services there was a small cadre of professionally trained nurses in the Queen Alexandra's Royal Naval Nursing Service (QARNNS) and the QARNNS Reserve.

By 5 August, Britain had been plunged into an even greater conflict than the one threatened in Ireland; it was to be total war in Europe. In a twist of political fate, the civil war in Ireland had been averted. Following discussions with the Prime Minister, John Redmond and Sir Edward Carson agreed that the Home Rule Bill would be suspended for the duration of the war. In politically astute moves, both sides took the opportunity to display their support for the war. Redmond and Carson hoped that their volunteers would be used for the war effort which, in turn, it was hoped, could lead to political gains. The northern Unionist and UVF volunteers hoped that by 'joining the colours' they would demonstrate loyalty to the crown and that a Protestant Ulster would be secured and maintained. Similarly, the Southern Irish and National Volunteers believed that if they supported and became involved in 'England's War', their loyalty would eventually be rewarded with the establishment of their own nation. In essence, one side fought to strengthen the union: the other to weaken it. It was against this background that three army divisions were raised in Ireland. From the predominantly Catholic south of the country came the 10th (Irish) Division, from the Protestant north the 36th (Ulster) Division, and the 16th (Irish) Division was comprised of battalions from the north and south of the country.

*The Nursing Times* prophetically lamented that 'what was nominally a quarrel between Austria and Serbia has led to a European Armageddon'. Suffragettes re-considered the militancy of their campaign and the political situation. The future fate of husbands, brothers and sons, and a sense of patriotic duty, complicated and overshadowed their franchise demands. One woman found no conflict of interest in her involvement with the Scottish Federation of Women's Suffrage Societies (SFWSS) and a desire to care for the casualties of war. Dr Elsie Inglis was a suffragist, and the Honorary Secretary of the SFWSS; she was also a committed doctor and humanitarian. At the outbreak of war, she was fifty years of age, and not in the best of health. With the enterprise, if not aggression, that the Scots are known for, Dr Inglis had set about forming the Scottish Women's Hospitals. The War Office rejected the offer of their services. They were, however, welcomed by the Allies and their units, staffed with volunteer doctors, nurses, drivers and orderlies from all over Britain and Ireland, and would serve in France and Serbia.

Britain was not prepared for war and, as in previous campaigns, the Royal Army Medical Corps and the Nursing Service were chronically short of trained personnel. The lessons of the Crimea and the Boer War regarding the treatment and disposal of battle casualties appear to have eluded the War Office planners – a point made by Mabel St Clair Stobart a few months earlier. As the British Expeditionary Force prepared to mobilise for war, it was medically ill-prepared for what was about to befall it. Adequate contingencies for the care of the sick and injured were not properly established, as nurses and doctors were later to discover. The French Army's 300,000 losses in the first month of the conflict should have alerted the War Office to the possibility that this was going to be a long and bloody war, and that all available skilled help would be needed. It would appear that a 'Land of Hope and Glory' psychology prevailed at the War Office.

Chapter III

## *'Good-bye-ee'*

# Men and Women of August 1914

August 1914 saw frantic political, military and social activity. On 5 August, the day after war was declared, the first War Council was held at 10 Downing Street. Field-Marshal the Earl Kitchener of Khartoum, a son of Tralee, Ireland, was appointed Secretary of State for War. Unlike others, Kitchener did not believe that 'it would all be over by Christmas' or 'before the leaves fall', and warned Asquith of a protracted and costly war, claiming that 'we must be prepared to put armies of millions in the field and maintain them for several years.' On that same day, Austria-Hungary declared war on Russia.

Britain had long depended on the might of the Royal Navy to defend her shores. On 5 August, Lord Northcliffe wrote an article for his newspaper, the *Daily Mail*, entitled, 'Not One British Soldier to Leave England's Shores'. Northcliffe maintained that the Royal Navy was the key to winning the conflict and some politicians supported his theory. However, those who believed the Royal Navy could fulfil all the defence requirements failed to appreciate that the forthcoming conflict would be primarily one of land warfare, fought by the army on foreign soil.

In 1914, Britain had a small, well-trained, regular army – but its size was not compatible with the demands about to be made on it. Between 1905 and 1912, under the direction of the Secretary of State for War, Richard Haldane (later to become Lord Haldane), the British Army had undergone a much-needed radical restructuring. Under the Haldane Reforms, the army was now organised into two distinct fighting units: for foreign incidents and conflicts, the men of the old regular army would form an Expeditionary Force (BEF); the defence of the British Isles would be undertaken by a Territorial Force (TF) and, if necessary, the TF would double its complement with volunteers.

In August 1914, the BEF, about to make its way to Belgium, consisted of six regular infantry divisions and a cavalry division, each of 20,000 troops. In addition, there were two regular infantry divisions, the Seventh and Eighth, which were garrison troops either recalled from around the Empire or surplus to domestic need; two divisions came from India. However, by 6 August, Parliament had sanctioned a further 500,000 men for the Army, and Canada had called for 20,000 volunteers to assist the war effort. On the day that Parliament was sanctioning additional men for military service, the National Union of Women's Suffrage Societies and the Women's Social and Political Union announced a suspension of all political and militant activities until the end of the war. Emmeline Pankhurst declared that:

> Our battles are practically over, we confidently believe. For the present at least our arms are grounded, for directly the threat of foreign war descended on our nation we declared a complete truce from militancy.

In Belgium, Liège's defensive ring of forts was partially penetrated by the German Second Army, and French troops entered German-controlled Lorraine. On 7 August the Germans entered Liège and the French Army entered Altkirch in Alsace. The British Expeditionary Force began to embark for France and Lord Kitchener called for the first 100,000 volunteers to support the Regular Army – the enlistment proposal was three years' service, or for the duration of the war.

On 8 August, 20,000 Canadians were accepted for war service. As the Belgian Army retreated along the River Dyle, and the French Army advanced against the German occupied city of Mulhouse in Alsace, an Editorial in *The Nursing Times* asked readers what 'the position of the nursing profession' would be. The question was tinged with more than a degree of interest as, with understandable but premature concerns, professional nurses were looking to the future.

Within the first few days of war being declared, it was estimated that in London alone 50,000 women from a variety of backgrounds, with little or no nursing experience, were volunteering to nurse the anticipated broken and bloodied bodies of the BEF. Included in this number were the society 'darlings' who had tangoed away the hours in plush hotels and posh parlours, and who now discovered they could have a more 'meaningful' way of occupying their time. According to one self-sacrificing individual, 'nursing seemed like a rather fun thing to do'.

Margaret Warren, a socialite from Surrey, epitomised the background of many of the women who volunteered for the nursing services.

> It was an absolutely wonderful life, all parties, all fun, all dances … we really had a gay life … everyone did. There was a sort of an idea of war, and people began thinking, should they do something; we used to have tennis parties and discuss what we could do …Then as time went on I

realized there would be a war, and so I went to various lectures and took the first-aid course and the home nursing course. My mother said 'whatever you do, you're not going to nurse; I'm not going to have you nursing'.

Margaret Warren defied her mother, and no doubt upset professionally-trained nurses, when she enlisted to become a volunteer nurse. Trained nurses jealously guarded their profession and they were fearful that, when the war ended, the unskilled, volunteer 'nurses' would swamp the labour market and affect their employment prospects. Nursing in peacetime was neither exciting nor glamorous, and the day-to-day ministrations of caring for the sick and injured brought little financial reward or public recognition. In the eyes of professional nurses, nursing was a vocation; volunteer nurses with limited training appeared to be devaluing the time and education invested, and the dedication and commitment shown, by trained nurses. In addition, they were concerned that professional development and the Nurse Registration Bill could be compromised. It was therefore not surprising that trained nurses had a problem with the volunteers whose motives for nursing were founded in wartime altruism. In spite of concerns for the future of professional nursing, an Editorial in *The Nursing Times* reflected on the current situation and sadly observed: 'The conflict will be terrible, and every soldier will be required for fighting and every nurse for the care of the wounded.' In a spirit of patriotism, if not professional determination, it concluded: 'The call has come and the nurses are ready.'

The 'call' for Sister Catherine Black came via the Matron of The London Hospital, who had promised the War Office fifty of her trained nurses for the care of the wounded. 'Blackie', as she was known to her colleagues, was on the staff of the hospital and had already volunteered for the QAIMNS. Sister Black was dispatched to The Cambridge Military Hospital at Aldershot. Her war had just begun.

On 9 August, under the command of Sir John French, the first units of the BEF landed in Boulogne. Due to strict censorship, it was a further week before an official dispatch informed the people of Britain and Ireland that 'the Expeditionary Force as detailed for Foreign Service has been safely landed on French soil. The embarkation, transportation and disembarkation of men and stores were alike carried through with the greatest precision and without a single casualty.' A public notice, drawn up by Felix Adam, Le Maire [Mayor] de Boulogne, was posted on walls and buildings, stating:

Arrival of the British Troops
Appeal to the Inhabitants
My dear Citizens, – This day arrive in our town the valiant British troops,

who come to cooperate with our brave soldiers to repel the abominable aggression of Germany. So before the invasion of the barbarians, all Europe rose against the like race who menaced the peace of the world and the security of other people. Boulogne, which is one of the homes of the Entente Cordiale, will give to the sons of the United Kingdom an enthusiastic and brotherly welcome. The citizens are requested on this occasion to decorate the fronts of their houses with the colours of the two countries.

The citizens of Boulogne, extending the warmest of welcomes to the BEF, had already sent their sons to war; the reservists of the 8th Boulogne Regiment had gone to Belgium, and had suffered considerable casualties. Such was the momentum of the war and its rising casualty lists, that by the time the BEF disembarked at Boulogne, French families had not yet received official notice stating that their sons, brothers, husbands and fathers were 'Dead on the Field of Honour'.

The men and 40,000 horses of the BEF arrived to enthusiastic welcomes in three separate ports: Boulogne, Le Havre and Rouen. Bunting, flags and flowers were everywhere and there was much cheering and singing by assembled crowds. The first detachment to arrive in France was the 2nd Battalion, Argyll and Sutherland Highlanders; they disembarked and marched to the rousing sound of 'Hielan' Laddie', 'Cock o' the North' and 'The Road to the Isles' played on their regimental pipes. As more and more of the old regular army arrived at Boulogne, the docks were hit by waves of khaki and tartan. Onlookers, casting an eye over the disembarking troops, would have seen a variety of army attire. In true Scottish military style, many of the regiments wore kilts. Some officers wore regimental tartan trews and the peaked Army Service cap was replaced in Scottish regiments with the Glengarry Bonnet. Prior to leaving for France, a decision was made by the Argylls that it would be diplomatic to give a bagpipe rendition of 'La Marseillaise' on arrival. As the assembled dignitaries and local crowds enthusiastically watched, the men formed up, and the pipers prepared their lungs for the first mighty blast of notes on their bagpipes.

Much to the annoyance and irritation of the Pipe Major, the opening bars of the French National anthem died a death in the drones and bladders of the pipes. The second attempt was successful and brought cheers and whistles from the crowds – the Auld Alliance was secured! A French brass band repaid the compliment and played 'God Save the King' and a ragtime version of 'Auld Lang Syne'. To the amusement of the troops and the embarrassment of their senior officers, French military and civilian officials, carried away by the emotion of the occasion, hugged and then kissed British Army officers on both cheeks – 'No tittering in the ranks' being the obvious command!

As the army battalions disembarked, the men marched to tunes ranging from old campaign songs to current popular musical hits. The journalist, George Curnock, who was on holiday near Boulogne when the BEF landed, claimed that 'they marched past, battalion after battalion ... shouting their slogans, whistling and singing their songs' and it was an Irish Regiment, the 2nd Battalion of the Connaught Rangers, which 'with a note of strange pathos in their rich Irish voices, sang a song I had never heard before:

It's a long Way to Tipperary
It's a long way to go.'

According to Curnock, a French woman standing beside him, on hearing the song, turned to him and said prophetically, 'Ah! The poor boys! ... A long, long way ... they don't know how long is the way they are going ... how long – how long.'

Accompanying the BEF to France was the Royal Army Medical Corps (RAMC). At the start of the hostilities the strength of the RAMC Regulars was 1,279 officers and 3,811 other ranks; the Territorial Force numbered 1,889 officers and 12,520 other ranks. In the Queen Alexandra's Imperial Military Nursing Service there were only 293 nurses, approximately 34 of them from Ireland. Compared with the rest of the army establishment, the number of serving nurses was minimal. It was considered unnecessary to have nursing sisters in every army hospital and barrack sick bay since they could be staffed by the medical orderlies of the RAMC under the direction of army doctors. The small elite group of nursing sisters of the QAIMNS was attached to larger army hospitals where skilled nursing care was needed for more serious medical and surgical conditions.

In August 1909, the War Office had launched a new scheme of voluntary aid organisations known as Voluntary Aid Detachments (VAD) to assist the work of the QAIMNS and the TFNS. The concept for it had emerged from the 1904–1905 Russo-Japanese War. Japan had organised its Army Medical Corps to a high degree of sophistication, putting science at the heart of military policy. Combating disease and the management of infected wounds became a research priority. As a result of their innovative thinking, morbidity and mortality rates amongst the Japanese troops fell dramatically. The Russian Army Medical Service was not so advanced; on the contrary, it was very basic. In order to render aid to the sick and wounded, Russian villagers volunteered to assist the established Army Medical Service. Inspired by the usefulness of Volunteer Aid, a number of countries subsequently adopted the practice. The British VAD were organised under the auspices of the British Red Cross Society which previously had been the British National Aid Society, formed

**This handkerchief was one of the many patriotic souvenirs produced to raise money for the War effort.**

in 1870 following the Franco-German War. In principle, their work consisted of providing very basic first-aid and their nursing training included home nursing, hygiene and sanitation.

A member of the VAD, Thekla Bowser who had been a serving sister in the Order of St. John since 1902, described the raison d'être of the VAD:

> ... to undertake such as supplying food and dressings for improvised ambulance trains, providing rest stations, running smaller hospitals and convalescent homes. It was realized that the members must be trained particularly in the art of improvisation and in coping with emergencies. Trained nurses must not be wasted. We are not untrained, but trained in a different way.

The range of health and welfare services which, in theory, would be available to the men of the BEF were to be tried and tested in the opening weeks of the war.

Between 14 and 24 August 1914, the last defensive fort at Liège in Belgium was destroyed. Namur had fallen and the German Army, marching through Belgium, implemented a policy of Shrecklichkeit (frightfulness) as they advanced. At Aerschot, German troops shot 150 civilians and carried out widespread violence against the population and their property. Further atrocities were carried out at Malines, Termonde, Melle, Huy, Tongres, Orsmael and St Trond. Cardinal Mercier circulated a letter requesting that, if possible, all Belgian convents should undertake to care for the casualties of war, including homeless and orphaned children. The Cardinal was insistent that, in administering nursing care to the sick and wounded, each convent should have at least three trained nurses working with the nuns.

At the Couvent de Ursuline in Thildonck, Reverend Mother Marie Georgine wrote lengthy descriptive letters about the emerging situation and the progress of the German invasion of Belgium. Between 16 and 20 August, she recorded:

> Whatever else we have to complain of, we can hardly complain of monotony at present, nor shall we be able to I fear for a long time to come ... Here the enthusiasm is so great that everyone is volunteering ... We received an alert that soldiers [Belgian] were coming to lodge in the village and that we should have to put up at least 800 here as well as the officers. There were 4000 of them in the village altogether, the 6th and 26th *de ligne* from Antwerp ... We had to send round to different farms for straw for them to sleep on ...
>
> They had numbers of men with them requiring attention so that the infirmary was regularly invaded. They had a military doctor and several Red Cross men with them but imagined that we had no provision for them

as we were not flying a Red Cross flag. When they found the true state of affairs and that we only required authorisation, they took the law into their own hands. They went up to the top of the house ... and fixed up a huge flag themselves. The sisters were up to unearthly hours of the night, washing their shirts, socks etc, which were a sight to behold, then came trousers to be mended, poor fellows, you should have seen the state they were in ... The soldiers have no idea where they are going or when or why and the officers themselves know very little more ... They were here two nights and finally received orders to leave next morning ... They left three sick men behind ... The men are most grateful for all that was done for them and some of the sick men made small offerings, 50 centimes, another 25 and so forth, because they said they had been kindly looked after. They had been told that the Germans aimed chiefly at the officers at Liège so that in certain regiments hardly an officer was left alive, so we made black linen covers for their shakos and swords and gold stripes so that there was nothing bright and shiny to aim at or distinguish them. I am so glad we did, for we were told yesterday that ours are the next to be sent to the front. Poor fellows, some of them have left their wives and children unprovided for ... one has been married just two days.

Apart from the small group of professionally trained army nurses, the women who went to Belgium and France in the first few weeks of the war were of independent means; some were trained nurses not attached to any particular service or organisation. Generally, however, they were middle or upper class women with little formal nursing training; some had first aid and home nursing certificates. They were part of a growing female, philanthropic, humanitarian movement which had emerged in the later part of the nineteenth century. Many were suffragists, quite a few were Quaker, and a few belonged to the Order of St John or the British Red Cross Society. They were described by Olive Dent, herself a VAD, as:

> Women, and indeed, girls of title, women who were known for their public services, professional women who abandoned work of lesser for that of greater importance, university graduates, as well as stay at home girls ... The majority spoke French; some fluent French and German... certificates included Institute of Hygiene, first-class advanced physiology, first-class cookery, full massage diplomas as well as BSc, BA and MA degrees.

While fluency in French and German may well have been extremely useful, and skills in cookery and massage would have their place in the care of the sick and wounded, by the middle of August, when the first British nursing dispatches were arriving in Belgium from Britain, it was clear that the greatest need was for trained nurses. A nurse from Ireland, who belonged to a small party of volunteer professional nurses, explained in a diary-letter the position they found themselves in before the fall of Dinant.

16th August 1914 – I am sure I will never forget the last twenty-four hours as long as I live. Of course, we had plenty to do before (slight wounds, exhaustion, pleurisy), but the worst began while some of us were trying to get to Mass and Holy Communion yesterday. The cannons have been going continually for thirty-six hours all around. The poor line regiments at Dinant are absolutely done; it would break your heart to see them; some of the men haven't had two hours sleep since Wednesday last. I dressed three poor fellows during the night – one with a bullet just above his heart; he was one of six left out of a company of 200 swept away at Dinant yesterday. The bullet went right through. Of course, we have no surgeons; the three doctors here are very good when they have time to come, but they don't pretend to be surgeons. Your heart would break with it all. I felt my eyes fill up so often during the time when I saw them gulp down the drink of water or coffee, or their poor feet one mass of blisters, some of them bleeding. Some of the worst get permission to let us bathe them and put some powder on before joining their companies again. One poor fellow, who had a bullet through his thigh we just had to bandage up hurriedly, as he had only half an hour, and had to go on to Givet in the ambulance … One of my patients told me he had to leave two of his comrades in a trench he managed to dig for them, with any food and drink he could find. That's the thought that makes one sad, the number that are lying in the trenches dying for want of a little attention. One dare not think too much about it.

18th August 1914 – Gave us all a choice of returning to London yesterday, just before this order came in force, as, of course, it was our last chance of getting back, but we mean to stay and see it out. Now, of course, it's risky, as the Germans respect nothing and no one. Still, it's here we are wanted most; there are lots of preparations, Red Cross hospitals, etc at the other side of the Meuse. Ours is the only place here … The other four nurses are absolutely dead beat, three of them lying on mattresses on the floor fast asleep. I can't sleep; I get about three hours out of the twenty-four, and the strangest part is that I don't seem to need more; the others say they don't know how I keep about; I don't know myself, except that it is no effort.

On the day the volunteer nurses were being given the chance to return to Britain, Sister Evelyn Luard, along with a Matron and 32 other QAIMNS nurses, departed from Dublin on the troop ship *SS City of Benares* for an 'unknown destination'. Accompanying the nurses were 600 soldiers and 200 men detailed for work in Field Ambulances. According to Sister Luard, who was a mature woman with years of nursing experience and also a Boer War veteran, the highlights of the trip for her were an impromptu concert staged by the soldiers and watching a soldier tenderly care for 'an angelic looking black puppy with a Red Cross on its collar'.

**A Matron and thirty-two Sisters of Queen Alexandra's Imperial Military Nursing Service on board the troopship SS City of Benares, leaving Dublin on their way to war. Sister Evelyn Luard was in this contingency.**

At Southampton docks, on 21 August, Sister Millicent Peterkin boarded the South American cargo ship, the *Anglo-Canadian*, where she wrote in her diary that 'there was neither accommodation or food on board'. The sleeping arrangements were basic and uncomfortable although 'the officers, engineers and stewards all gave up their bunks to us, but the majority of the party had to sleep on their holdalls and rugs on the deck, and some in one of the lifeboats.' Apart from the unsuitability of the sleeping arrangements, it was also very noisy and wet. 'We were loading a lot of remounts, so the noise all night was terrific, and all were not on board until 3 or 4 a.m. by which time a fog had come on, making everything very wet.' After twenty-four hours on the ship Sister Peterkin disembarked at Le Havre on 22 August, following what she described as 'a triumphal progress up river and through docks, cheered by crowds ... and Tommies, very cheerful, singing 'Tipperary' and returning cheers.'

The same day, at Casteau, north-east of Mons, the first British troops, the 4th Royal Irish Dragoon Guards, went into action. Sergeant Thomas of the Royal Irish recounted their first engagement with Germans.

I saw a troop of Uhlans coming leisurely down the road, the officer in front smoking a cigar. We were anxiously watching their movements when they halted as if they smelt a rat. They had seen us! They turned quickly back. Captain Hornby got permission to follow on with the sabre troops, and down the road they galloped. My troop was ordered to follow on in support, and we galloped on through the little Village of Casteau ... we could see the 1st Troop using their swords and scattering the Uhlans.

Referred to as 'The Mounted Micks', the 4th Royal Irish were known to be hard fighters, drinkers and swearers; their first claim to military fame was said to have taken place in 1736 in Dublin where they enthusiastically charged 40 punch bowls, and achieved their objective in less than fifteen minutes! Their next claim to fame would be that they were the first British troops in action in Belgium and, during their engagement with the Germans, the first British Army rifle shot was fired by Sergeant Thomas who was a drummer at the time. He said, as an explanation of his dual role:

> I find lots of people think bandsmen are not soldiers in the ordinary sense, but they are quite wrong, for every bandsman has got to do his military duties in addition to his musical ones, and the moment war comes he has to turn from his musical instruments to his weapon of battle.

Many bandsmen were used as regimental stretcher-bearers and they had a gruesome and, at times, thankless job. A general was later to remark that if he had a thousand Victoria Crosses to distribute, all would go to stretcher-bearers.

In Belgium, on 23 August at Mons, the historic capital of the ancient Duchy of Hainault, the first major battle between the BEF and German armies took place. The BEF was greatly outnumbered, but fought for seven hours and sustained 1,400 casualties before the order to retire was given. The retreat lasted until 5 September, with devastating consequences for the Expeditionary Force.

August was one of the hottest months in years and the army service uniform was inappropriate for the weather or for a retreat at speed. The men wore heavy boots and carried 60–80 pounds of equipment and ammunition. Corporal John Denore of the 1st Royal Berkshire Regiment stated that on 26 August, 'we marched all day long, miles and miles it seemed, probably owing to the fact that we had no sleep at all since Saturday the 22nd.' On 27 August he noticed that the marching was 'getting quite disorderly; numbers of other men from other regiments were mixed up with us' and men were starting to 'throw away their overcoats'. The next day he reported that 'the men were discarding their equipment in a wholesale fashion.' By 31 August, the BEF were still in retreat and fighting a rearguard action. The men, by now, had resorted to marching in their socks, others had wrapped their puttees round their feet instead of boots. Denore said that the men:

... marched until they dropped ... but one man found a mouth-organ and despite the fact that his feet were bound in blood-soaked rags, he staggered along at the head of the company playing tunes all day. Mostly he played the 'The Irish Emigrant' which is a good marching tune.

Throughout the fall-back the army was shedding everything it possessed; the need for speed and the welfare of the men and horses, hungry, thirsty and exhausted, were more important than army equipment.

The Army medical and nursing services were to suffer a similar fate; fully equipped mobile hospitals which had been established at Boulogne had to be abandoned. They were re-established at Le Havre, but they too had to be evacuated. The evacuation line established for the casualties of the Mons retreat was initially through Amiens and Rouen, but confusion and quantity of numbers hampered the effectiveness of the evacuation plans. Amiens was congested with refugees, and soldiers of the British, French and Belgian Armies who were passing through on troop trains or were temporarily billeted in the city. Sister Peterkin, who was now nursing the casualties of Mons, described the retreat:

> About 5 p.m. a train from Amiens passed through, bound for Le Havre, loaded with refugees, and wounded British soldiers. The latter were lying eight or nine in each truck, and in beside each lot were two sisters from No. 7 General Hospital. They had to fly from Amiens, abandoning 700 beds, all their tents and equipment, and all personal belongings, having nothing but what they stood in.

In a dispatch sent back to Britain, a Welsh nurse, who had gone to France on the same ship as Millicent Peterkin, described the effect that the Mons retreat was having on the working conditions:

> Here we were for two days and on the third we were moved to an empty Convent school, where we are now awaiting orders to fix up our hospital, which comprises of 21 surgeons, 44 sisters and nurses and 120 orderlies. Just outside this town are already two hospitals at work in tents. Last night one came in from Amiens with their sick and wounded in the train with them. They had been obliged to leave in a great hurry, hearing that the enemy were not far off. They left their tents and luggage (and their tea which was just ready!) and came in their caps and aprons just as they were.

Doctor Arthur Osborne of the Royal Army Medical Corps was initially unaware of the order to retire, and was working without the support of other doctors. He was inundated with casualties and was struggling to render care.

In streams the wounded poured in, some walking, some carried pick-a-back or in hand seats, and a few on stretchers … Where were the doctors? There seemed to be not a sign of one! I did not realise, then, the almost hopeless task that the infantry doctors were engaged in. My orderly and myself made desperate attempts to cope with the streams of wounded men. The whole of the cart sheds were now full of wounded that lay or sat about in the mud and sodden straw. Every post was being clung to by those able to stand; some slipped down and fainted. There were now streams of men, presumably wounded, passing right and left across the fields: I knew not to where. It never occurred to me that anyone was retreating. We must have been there for hours, but it seemed only a few minutes before we were lighting candles and lanterns to see what we were doing. So numerous now were the wounded that I could only find time to look at the worst, and then do little more than tighten an amateur tourniquet or plug a gaping wound in the chest wall with gauze, and give morphia, in heroic doses to those who appeared to be in the most pain … Getting suddenly alarmed at all the possibilities, I hurriedly collected my gear, and we mounted, leaving, alas, many wounded, some partly and others quite unattended. I left them in charge of a senior non-commissioned officer of infantry who was only slightly wounded. I reminded him of the most simple forms of tourniquets and, giving him an armful of dressings, advised him when the carts came back to move all the rest of the wounded to Thulin.

Casualties who could not mobilise were, after some rudimentary first-aid, left to fend for themselves, or to the mercy of the advancing German army. Sister Peterkin claimed a wounded British officer she was nursing said he saw 'Germans killing their own wounded as well as British and French'.

As the BEF were retreating from Mons, the sacking of the city of Louvain began. The city had been occupied by the Germans since 19 August, but, panicked into believing that an allied attack was imminent, they set about terrorising and murdering the citizens. For five days the people of Louvain lived in fear for their lives; they witnessed the savage destruction of their homes, the Palais de Justice, the University with its renowned library of ancient manuscripts, the Church of St Pierre, the Academie des Beaux-Arts and the Commercial and Consular Science buildings. The small villages in and around the Louvain area were plundered and burnt, and the inhabitants were subjected to excessive barbarity. Reverend Mother Marie Georgine described the behaviour of the Germans.

The horrors committed at Wespelaer defy description, and the poor Curé [priest] had aged twenty years when we last saw him bringing a poor cancerous woman, whom they had shot (after killing her mother and brother), here to be looked after. The poor creature had been two days in a ditch unable to get help. The Germans saw her but would do nothing and no one else dared to venture out of doors.

Murders, rapes, lootings and incendiarism by the German troops were to continue. Reverend Mother Marie Georgine continued to catalogue them and to treat the victims.

On 1 September, according to Corporal Denore:

We continued at the same game from dawn till dark, and dark till dawn – marching and fighting and marching. Every roll call there were fewer and fewer to answer; some were killed, some wounded, and some who had fallen out were missing.

On 3 September he lamented:

It was the most terrible march I have ever done. Men were falling down like nine-pins. They would fall flat on their faces on the road, while the rest of us staggered round them, as we couldn't lift our feet high enough to step over them, and, as for picking them up, that was impossible, as to bend meant to fall. What happened to them, God only knows.

At home, there was a rush of public enthusiasm to help war casualties and to establish hospital beds for the sick and injured. Women of all ages and social backgrounds formed volunteer groups preparing bandages and lint for the war hospitals at home and abroad and making comfort garments for sick and injured troops. According to *The Nursing Times*, the general philosophy was 'Those who cannot nurse can sew.' In London, the Homeopathic Hospital placed 163 beds at the disposal of the Admiralty. The Board of Trustees offered the War Office the use of Crystal Palace as a hospital which, it was claimed, could accommodate 5,000 sick and injured soldiers as well as supplying living and sleeping arrangements for medical and nursing staff. Lambeth Palace, the home of the Archbishop of Canterbury, was offered as a war emergency hospital. Lady Esher conducted classes on first-aid and home nursing at the Duke of York's Barracks, Chelsea, Queen Amelie of Portugal enrolled as a member of the British Red Cross and the Duchess of Teck was a volunteer nurse at Knightsbridge Barracks. The Duchess of Westminster, along with Lady Sarah Wilson and the former mistress of Edward VII, Mrs Alice Keppel, organised base hospitals. According to one notice, London ladies were offering accommodation for invalid seamen and many were willing to place their whole houses at the disposal of the Admiralty. Mrs Claude Watney gave up part of her house in Berkeley Square for the care of naval and military officers; the facility it was claimed was 'fully equipped with all the requirements for modern surgery' and was staffed by 'fully trained nurses'.

In Grimsby, much to the delight of the local children, all schools were converted into hospitals, as was the local theatre. Newcastle prepared 4,000 beds for the reception of any wounded brought from the North Sea. With help from Queen Mary, the Palace Hotel, Southend, was being turned into a Royal Naval Hospital. In Manchester, technical and secondary schools were placed in the hands of the military authorities for use as war hospitals. In Yarmouth, the General Hospital was making ready thirty beds for the wounded men of the BEF and, in Liverpool, equipment and provisions were gathered to supply a 600-bed facility. The University of Birmingham was adapted as a military hospital, creating 520 beds for war casualties.

In Scotland, courtesy of the King, Balmoral Castle was placed at the disposal of the War Office for use as a hospital for wounded soldiers and sailors. In Edinburgh Castle, an ordnance store, which thirty years earlier had been converted into a hospital, was commandeered for military casualties. The efficiency of the St Andrew's Ambulance Association had all the military hospitals in Scotland staffed within forty-eight hours of war being declared. The hospital ship, *St Margaret of Scotland*, was equipped by a grateful nation raising £22,000; it was agreed with the naval authorities that the ship would be staffed by Scottish medical officers and orderlies. As part of the Territorial Reserve, trained nurses from the Royal Infirmary of Edinburgh received notification of mobilisation and said goodbye to their families and friends at Waverley Station, as had their Royal Infirmary colleague Sister Peterkin, who was now in the thick of the Mons retreat.

Ireland, it was claimed, was 'straining every nerve' to send its quota of trained nurses for any war service work that was needed. The extent of professionally trained nurses offering their services was described by the Irish Correspondent of *The Nursing Times* as 'hardly a nurse to be got here for private cases for love or money – all volunteering'. In Dublin, according to the same journal:

> Various large general hospitals were taking in ladies of social position for short training ... We hope, however, that all this may not get overdone and that Ireland may not suffer from an overplus of first aiders to the neglect of other ways of helping ... They all seem to fly to amateur nursing, and there is bound to be disappointment. Of course if they content themselves with looking after the ordinary sick in hospitals and so free regular nurses, it will be all right.

The description 'ordinary sick' in *The Nursing Times* is as interesting as it is puzzling; who were 'the ordinary sick'? Clearly, a hierarchy of patients, as well as nurses, was beginning to evolve.

An official line-up of a Matron with nursing sisters, VAD nurses, probationer nurses, a nun
nursing sister, Royal Army Medical Corps doctors, stretcher-bearers and medical orderlies.

There was evidence of a growing compulsion to nurse emerging from the
women of Britain and Ireland. Applications to the QAIMNS, the QAIMNS
Reserve, TFNS, Queen Alexandra's Royal Naval Nursing Service
(QARNNS), the QARNNS Reserve and The British Red Cross Society came
from every social background while information on how to volunteer for
active service was given in nursing journals.

WHERE TO VOLUNTEER
Nurses wishing to volunteer for active service must do so at the office of
the British Red Cross Society, which is now established at Devonshire
House, Piccadilly, by the kindness of the Duke of Devonshire, who has
placed the whole of the ground floor at the disposal of the Committee, or
through the St John's Ambulance Association, St John's Gate,
Clerkenwell. Nurses engaged in hospitals or on the staff of Private
Nursing Institutions, or District Nursing Associations, should first get the
assent of the Matron or Superintendent. The Medical Department of the
Admiralty state that many applications are made there by nurses of
varying qualifications. The authorities are not in need of nurses, or
desirous of enrolling them, and it is unlikely that their services will be
utilised if offered there. Many hundreds of applications are also made at
the War Office. In both instances, applications should be made through
the British Red Cross Society. Applications for enrolment in the
International Nursing Corps for Active Service in War, from three years

certificated nurses, should be made at the Headquarters of the International Council of Nurses, 431 Oxford Street, London.

At the outbreak of the war, when the Government delegated the responsibility for organising voluntary nursing services to the British Red Cross Society, this led to bitter resentment and hostility between the National Council of Trained Nurses and the British Red Cross Society. The situation between the two organisations did not improve, and as the weeks progressed, the antipathy between the trained and volunteer nurses worsened. In spite of the rising animosity between them, and encouraged by public support, the determination of the Red Cross remained unchanged. The secretary of the British Red Cross Society claimed that, in the first two weeks of war, their headquarters at Devonshire House, London, was 'absolutely swamped' with all kinds of offers, and the VAD had raised and registered at the War Office 1,900 detachments with a personnel of 60,000. All this activity took place before Queen Alexandra, as President of the British Red Cross Society, made a public appeal for funds towards the care and relief of sick and wounded troops. In her national appeal, the Queen asked her subjects to consider that a war 'has been forced upon us greater and more terrible even than the Napoleonic wars which devastated Europe one hundred years ago'.

> Thousands of our brave sailors and soldiers are standing ready to defend Britain's shores and to uphold her honour. Their sufferings will be great, and it is to us that they will look for comfort and relief. That comfort must not be denied them. As President of the British Red Cross Society I appeal for your help. I do it knowing that you will respond to this appeal in the name of humanity. Much money will be needed and many gifts if we are faithfully to discharge our trust and be able to say when all is over that we have done all we could do for the comfort and relief of our sick and wounded. The heart of the great British Nation will surely and generously go out to those who are so gallantly upholding the cause of their country.

In late August when Lord Kitchener made a further appeal for volunteers, 174,901 young men joined up in a single week. Between August and September the daily enlistment rose from 10,019 to 33,000. Some young society males, driven to patriotic posturing on the national bandwagon of war euphoria, joined the services and immediately aligned themselves to the officer class. Having sought commissions, they became caricatures of the military's privileged classes. Some of the 'war service' enthusiasts absurdly believed that in order to 'do their bit' more effectively, they needed to acquire impedimenta such as monocles, swords, wide breeches and a manner of speech where everything was 'absolutely too much bally fag, what?' These pretentious and naïve young men would soon discover that accoutrements and a manner of speech were no defence against an obscene death. They were caricatured in the theatre as 'Gilbert the Filbert' by the actor, Basil Hallam Radford. Radford himself was to serve and die in France in 1916.

The mobilisation plan of the BEF had turned out to be very successful although their first enemy encounter and subsequent retreat resulted in many casualties. However, as General Sir George Cowans, the Quartermaster General, was to discover, the overall mobilisation and recruitment plan was challenged by practicalities; military planners had failed to address the practical issues of training, equipping, housing and feeding an expanding defence force. Before the outbreak of war, the Ordnance Service had annually provided the regular army with a quarter of a million pairs of boots, two hundred and twenty thousand shirts and a million pairs of socks. With the establishment and expansion of the 'Kitchener' armies, Cowans and his team had to find similar quantities in a week!

Medical supplies were vital; millions of vaccines had to be obtained, and administered to the troops. Hospitals and casualty clearing stations had to be established, equipped and staffed. A fleet of ships was employed for the transportation of the sick and injured, and they too required doctors, nurses, medical orderlies and equipment as did the ambulance trains that were commissioned. An army may march on its belly, but morale is derived from the belief that should soldiers become casualties of war, they will be adequately cared for. Cowans knew the wisdom of that psychology and, at times against political and economic odds and objections, did his best to secure the health and welfare of the troops. Lloyd George was later to describe Jack Cowans as a soldier and man who:

> ... discharged his duties throughout the four and a half years of the War in such a way as to give complete satisfaction to everybody concerned, soldiers and civilians. Whatever the doubts and grumbles there were about deficiencies and shortcomings of other war leaders, there was never a murmur from any quarter as to the efficiency with which Sir John Cowans did his work.

In the columns of the *British Journal of Nursing*, professional nurses continued to snipe at the competence of Red Cross nurses. The Editor, Ethel Bedford Fenwick was becoming more and more vociferous about the work of the VAD, subjecting it to a fair amount of scrutiny and scorn.

> In the grim struggle now proceeding on the battle fields of Europe thousands of brave men must of necessity be stricken down, of whom

many will be cared for in hospitals at home or abroad. Upon the type of care which they there receive will largely depend their chances of life itself, as well as, in many cases, whether their recovery is complete or incomplete. It is therefore a grave national duty not only that fully trained and experienced nurses should be provided to nurse our sick and wounded troops at home and abroad in sufficient numbers, but also that unauthorised nurses should be prevented from proceeding to the seat of war and monopolizing places which should be filled by those whose qualifications have been examined and tested ...We hope that Lord Kitchener who dealt effectively with this abuse in South Africa will make a similar stand against it in Europe so far as British troops are concerned. The lives of our soldiers, and those of our Allies, are too precious to be left to the chance ministrations of unauthorised persons whose assurance may only be surpassed by their incapacity.

While nursing politics were being played out in the pages of professional journals, the reality of nursing the sick and wounded in Belgium and France was reflected in the nursing dispatches and diaries that were being sent back home.

Large convoy arrived about four thirty, every tent soon full. Three Germans included in numbers (about 400), all badly wounded. One has been injured nine days before and had been hiding so condition of the wound can be imagined. Many of our own men are in a similar state, some with wounds a week old, all have been at least four days and nights on train, open cattle trucks and horse boxes with no conveniences of any kind. This is how they always come, poor wretches. One man has both feet shot through and they are now hopelessly gangrenous, smell awful, of course they will have to come off, many other similar cases. They say that the wounded lie for days up at the front, with no one taking any notice of them. It is a notorious fact!

The account above of the casualty care arrangements was made by Sister Peterkin, and delays and lack of treatment was supported by Sister Luard's experiences.

You board a cattle truck, armed with a tray of dressings and a pail; the men were lying on straw, had been in trains for several days. Most had only been dressed once, and many were gangrenous ... They were nearly all shrapnel-shell wounds more ghastly than I have ever seen or smelt; the Mauser wounds of the Boer War were pinpricks compared with them.

The delay in emergency medical aid was commonplace – and unacceptable. The condition of some casualties was aggravated by the deficiencies and inadequacies of medical and nursing services. The limitations of professional care were becoming more and more apparent, but it would take four more months of fighting before the rudiments of a properly organised medical and nursing service could adequately and humanely deal with injured, sick and dying soldiers.

For the exhausted, sick and wounded members of the BEF, the retreat from Mons did not mean defeat: there were glimmers of the indefatigable nature of the old regular army. Major Tom Bridges had collected the stragglers from the different regiments, and was aware that the men were too hungry and exhausted to march. Having been separated from their regiments in the retreat, the men were demoralised. Bridges knew the dispirited soldiers needed motivation.

> The men were so jaded; it was pathetic to see them. If one only had a band, I thought. Why not? There was a toy shop handy which provided my trumpeter and myself with a tin whistle and a drum, and we marched round and round the fountain where the men were lying like dead, playing 'The British Grenadiers' and 'Tipperary', and beating the drum like mad. They sat up and began to laugh and even cheer … They began to stand up and fall in, and eventually we moved slowly off into the night to the music of our improvised band, now reinforced with a couple of mouth-organs.

Music, humour, self-deprecation and compassion – Major Bridges had found the right balance in the psychology of motivation. In addition, it was an example of the indomitable human spirit that was to see men and women survive the war on the Western Front over the next four years.

Chapter IV

## *'Keep the Home Fires Burning'*

# Western and Home Fronts 1914

From August to November 1914 the war was no longer a war of rapid movement but a war of stalemate. From Belgium to Switzerland the belligerent nations dug in, entrenching their armies along a 475-mile continuous line. It became known as the Western Front where, over the next four years, military objectives would be bitterly and brutally contested and, in the process, men and women would become disabled and disfigured and the landscape destroyed.

In the first five months of the war, the BEF sustained 177,423 casualties. Of these 98,866 were battle casualties which included those classed as missing or held as prisoners of war, those killed, wounded or those who died of wounds. The remaining 78,557 were non-battle casualties whose death, injuries or illness did not result from enemy action.

From August to December 1914, between battle and non-battle, for the BEF there were 1,160 casualties per day. Given the numbers of men needing skilled medical and nursing intervention, it is not surprising that the medical and nursing services claimed to be totally overwhelmed. In the autumn and early winter months of 1914, men were being treated for non-battle conditions such as tuberculosis, tetanus, meningitis, dysentery, eye and ear infections, varicose veins, pneumonia, hernia, rheumatism, tonsillitis and venereal disease. Battle wounds were caused by rifles or machine guns, shells, bombs, grenades and bayonets.

The daily admissions and discharge book of Number 14 Field Ambulance highlighted the conditions from which soldiers were suffering in the first few months of war. (See overleaf)

Cases of enteric fever which the Army Medical Services believed to be carried by refugees and the civilian population were becoming more frequent. One RAMC Medical Officer who thought differently lodged his concerns about the totally inadequate sanitary arrangements and the effect they were having on the health of the troops and the environment. He wrote:

# Admission and Discharge Book

## 14 Field Ambulance Hospital

Note: Names and service numbers have been removed to protect anonymity.

| Ad-mission | Regiment | Rank | Completed Years | | Disease |
|---|---|---|---|---|---|
| | | | Age | Service | |
| 181 | Royal Army Medical Corps | Private | 32 | 15 | Boils |
| 182 | RAMC | Private | 18 | 1 | Tonsillitis |
| 183 | Royal Field Artillery | Gunner | 24 | 9/12 | Fractured leg |
| 184 | Suffolks | Lance/C | 26 | 8 | Vomiting |
| 185 | Suffolks | Private | 39 | 19 | Gout |
| 186 | Surreys | Private | 29 | 11 | NYD* |
| 187 | Manchester | Private | 29 | 8 | Diarrhoea |
| 188 | Manchester | Lance/C | 20 | 2 | NYD* |
| 189 | Manchester | Lance/C | 31 | 11 | Diarrhoea |
| 190 | Suffolks | Private | 28 | 10 | NYD* |
| 191 | Dorset | Private | 19 | 2 | NYD* |
| 192 | Manchester | Private | 32 | 10 | Hernia |
| 193 | Royal Field Artillery | Private | 34 | 10 | Abscess/ Leg |
| 194 | Royal Field Artillery | Corporal | 33 | 13 | Boils |
| 195 | Dorsets | Private | 30 | 11 | NYD* |
| 196 | Royal Engineers | Sergeant | 35 | 17 | Lumbago |
| 197 | Royal Field Artillery | Gunner | 21 | 3 | Gonorrhoea |
| 198 | Army Service Corps | Private | 35 | 10 | Sciatica |
| 199 | Gordon Highlanders | Private | 21 | 3 | Gunshot Abdomen |
| 200 | Royal Scots | Corporal | 33 | 15 | Gunshot thigh |
| 201 | Royal Scots | Private | 28 | 9 | Gunshot head |
| 202 | Gordon Highlanders | Private | 34 | 12 | Gunshot chest |
| 203 | Manchester | Private | 28 | 11 | Abrasions |

NYD meant Not Yet Diagnosed. Later in the war there was an addition to this category which would read NYD (N) – Not Yet Diagnosed (Neurological)

The sanitary condition of the railway station at Abbeville is indescribable. The whole area of the railway line within a mile of the station is covered with faeces and filth of every description. This condition of things is principally due to the troops who have passed through the station previous to our arrival. Two sanitary squads have been at work on it since yesterday but have made little impression on it yet. Nothing less than a fatigue party of at least 100 men with the necessary shovels, brushes, picks, etc. will be of any use at the present juncture. They will be required to systematically sweep up and bury, or burn, faeces and refuse from a square half mile of ground. When this is done, proper latrines with screens and cover must be provided for the use of troops passing through, as the ordinary station latrines are quite inadequate and are required by the civilian passengers.

It is possible to dig temporary latrines in the spaces between the lines for the present, and this is being done, but screens for these are urgently required. Without screens, trenches are avoided by the troops and they always seek the shelter of a railway truck or fence. This matter is one of extreme urgency as among the divisions who have presumably passed through the station there have been several cases of Enteric Fever. Until the station is thoroughly cleaned up, therefore, it is standing menace to the health of the troops. To prevent a recurrence of this extensive fouling of the ground, sentries should be posted at intervals on the railway lines with definite orders to prevent men defecating on the ground.

Unfortunately for the troops, by denying the inadequacies of the sanitation system, the War Office was burying its head in the sand. Deficiencies in the sanitary arrangements could just as easily lose a man his dignity and his life, as would exposure to shells, bombs and bullets. Arguments, denials and recriminations rumbled on until October when a new sanitary management system was implemented. A RAMC medical officer assigned to oversee the new arrangements claimed:

> The general sanitation of each army is under the supervision of an expert attached to its Director of Medical Services, while in each division there is a special sanitary section, the officer commanding it acting as sanitary expert, and advising on sanitary matters connected with the division and its component battalion and other units. Each of these sanitary sections has a small staff of non-commissioned officers and men, with plenty of equipment, such as disinfecting machines, which accompany the division wherever it goes.

That was the plan – the reality was different. The sanitary arrangements in the trenches were such that latrines were created by digging pits of four or five feet. When they were nearly full, the pits were filled in and new pits were established. The pit latrines were managed by the sanitary squad, commonly known as 'shit wallahs'. Buckets were used as an alternative to 'shit pits' and again it was the role of the sanitation orderly to remove the buckets of urine and faeces and bury them away from the trenches. Due to the exigencies of trench life and combat conditions, this was not always possible and 'Gardez l'eau' arrangements prevailed. The sanitary arrangements were crude, basic, and not immune from enemy shelling. When men claimed it was a 'shitty war', it often meant just that.

From the time hostilities began in August 1914 to December of that year, the combined British, French and Belgian forces sustained more than one million casualties. Collectively, and quite often literally, they haemorrhaged about 68,000 casualties per day; this was unparalleled in the history of warfare. The War Office had consistently failed to respond to requests for help and logistical support from the medical and nursing services. Given that the 'conservation of manpower' was one of the Army's main aims, the health promotion and medical arrangement policies were a complete contradiction of their stated objectives. By not responding to the requests for aid, the War Office was creating problems for everyone, particularly the already overworked medical and nursing services.

The equation was clear: medically neglected casualties of war took longer to recover and rehabilitate; therefore treatment became costlier both in manpower and financing. Delayed access to care subsequently meant that the military 'efficiency' of the combatant was reduced.

Casualty care was compromised by a lack of cooperation between the War Office and the medical authorities. In addition to this, there was insufficient information, poor equipment, and a lack of strategic planning in the care and disposal of casualties as they passed through various handling systems. It would appear that all efforts to relieve the distress of sick and injured troops were hampered by a dogma of false, if not petty, politics and economics. In much understated language, the arrangements within the casualty clearing system were later described as being 'rudimentary and unsatisfactory'. It was not surprising that there was widespread criticism of medical arrangements. Following the retreat from Mons and the subsequent battles of the Marne and Aisne, Colonel Arthur Lee of the RAMC prepared a series of reports on the sub-standard medical arrangements and the effect they had on the welfare of the Medical Officers:

> The Royal Army Medical Corps were undoubtedly overworked and over strained. There were probably not enough Medical Officers in the first place, and many had been killed or wounded ... The shortage of Medical Officers is very apparent to the layman during these periods of great stress. It is difficult to get the RAMC to represent this. They seldom if ever complain and they work on until they drop with fatigue. But, apart from the fact that cases coming into the Clearing Hospitals have often to wait unnecessarily long before their wounds can be dressed, I have frequently seen Medical Officers who have been working for such long periods, without sleep or proper food, that they are not in a fit condition to attend to the serious cases.

Because of this, there were serious concerns about the physical and psychological health of the medical officers. One observer was equally concerned about 'the tired, haggard and unshaven men, unwashed, plastered with mud, many in little more than rags' who were holding the line.

The inadequacies of the medical arrangements were reinforced by the nursing dispatches that were arriving on the Home Front. From September to December 1914, nurses detailed the difficulties they had with casualty handling, evacuation and sanitation. In addition they claimed there were not enough nurses, facilities and equipment to help with the care of the sick and wounded. A nursing sister described a scene of damaged and neglected humanity at a dockside warehouse in Boulogne:

> I stared horror struck at the scene which met my eyes when I went on duty one evening. Embarkation had started; men on crutches, blind men with eyes bandaged, clung to the shoulder of the man in front in one long column; their clothes were clogged with mud and dried blood; they stumbled over figures lying either dead or asleep on the floor of the huge warehouse; some were actually crawling on hands and knees in case they got left behind. Finally there came the stretcher-bearers with the badly wounded, their grey expressionless faces fallen in and hollow cheeked. The miserable procession brought from the slimy black mire of no man's land seemed endless.

Delivering nursing care in different geographical areas and environments highlighted to nurses the widespread deficiencies in the casualty care system. It was not only, however, where or how they worked that angered and distressed the nurses, but also when they could work. Nurses were aware that there was a great deal of under-utilisation of their skills and they knew that, in many circumstances, men were waiting for days, and in some cases weeks, before they received access to proper care. One sister lamented:

> All the time the men have been dying in the trenches and elsewhere for the want of good nursing, there have been dozens of nurses waiting in Paris for the work they might do. It made one's heart ache to think of it.

While on No. 5 Hospital Train, Sister Luard described in her diary the complications of delayed access to medical intervention and the physical, if not psychological, effort it required to care for her patients:

> Shall I ever forget the stretchers coming in. Not a sound, only their eyes moved. Icy cold they were, badly wounded, patiently enduring. They had been in the train [troop] three or four days, some had been wounded for three weeks, no attention but the first field dressing, the wounds of many pouring with pus; typhoid and scarlet fever amongst them ... The glorious British Army lying broken in the train sleep (or the chance of it) three hours one night and four the next with all the hours between hard working putting the British Army together again.

Before the censor was able to halt the flow of mail describing what the war correspondent Philip Gibb called 'the realities of war', the letters and dispatches being sent home by nurses were unanimous in their condemnations and concerns about the casualty care system, and how it was ineffectively planned and managed. The medical arrangements had consistently failed to secure urgent supplies that were needed for the humane treatment and care of casualties. In a gesture of support for the over-stretched medical services, Lady Bagot, a woman of social position and influence, personally had taken cases of chloroform to Belgium, but the lack of anaesthesia had become a serious problem. A sister claimed that:

> The mere idea that men who have been badly injured should be subjected to unnecessary pain because the supply of the strongest anaesthetic has given out is heartbreaking. We cannot quite understand how such a dilemma as this has arisen.

The serious shortage of trained doctors, nurses and medical supplies was, to some extent, lost in the petty arguments and comments that were taking place in the medical and nursing journals. The *British Medical Journal* claimed it had been 'reliably informed' that '2000 dressings a day were being changed by a detachment of untrained women at the front.' The nursing journals kept up their campaign against the untrained VAD nurses, peppering their columns with vitriol, gossip and hearsay.

> A friend of mine told me that a large house she knows has been turned into a hospital for wounded, and the two daughters of the house were doing wonders, one aged fifteen, the other aged seventeen(!!). They were now able to get all the dressings ready for the surgeons and prepare the theatre, operation table etc! Will the doctors and public never wake up?

The vitriol, gossip and hearsay were of little relevance on the Western Front where doctors and nurses faced the realities of the everyday struggle to maintain the preservation of life and limb by whatever means possible. After lying unattended for days with flies and maggots crawling around and into their suppurating wounds, did soldiers really care about the use of 'untrained women'? The shortage of skilled help required everyone to do what they could. The level of debate and responses published in the medical and nursing journals made it clear that anyone who had any practical front line experience would know the value of deft hands, even if they were untrained. It was the presence of a small VAD unit in France which apparently upset those making the biggest noise from the comfortable and secure positions of their armchairs. Rachel Crowdy, a trained nurse and VAD member, identified that rest rooms at French railway stations could give VAD volunteers the chance to contribute to the health and welfare of the troops. In October 1914, under the supervision of Katharine Furse, a friend of Miss Crowdy, three trained nurses and eighteen volunteers established in French railway wagons a dispensary, kitchen and Quartermaster's store. Within twenty-four hours of becoming operational, 1,000 wounded men had been fed. Following a request from the Railway Transport Officer, within a week, the trained nurses and volunteers were tending to the sick and injured that required overnight shelter. The nurses commandeered railway carriages and turned them into makeshift dressing stations. The small unit set about feeding the wounded and the trained nurses, supported by volunteers, changed the men's dressings.

As nurses and volunteers in VAD units were subjected to harsh discipline and stringent rules governing their behaviour, both on overseas and Home Front service, it is hard to understand why there was such concern about their involvement. Life was not easy for VADs posted on overseas service and their living arrangements were basic. The regulations governing the employment of nursing VAD members in military hospitals clearly show not only how difficult it was to be accepted for service in the first place but also the control that was exercised over recruits:

Selected nursing members must be thoroughly recommended as in every way suitable to be employed in the Wards of Military Hospitals, and must be willing to be so employed under the following conditions.

1.   They will be required to work under fully trained Nurses, and will be under the direct control of the Officer in Charge and the Matron of the Hospital in which employed.
2.   Their duties will be similar to those carried out by probationers in Civil Hospitals. These include sweeping, dusting, polishing of brasses, cleaning of ward tables and patients' lockers, cleaning of ward sinks and ward utensils, washing of patients' crockery and sorting of linen. These, and any nursing duties which they are considered qualified to perform, will be allotted to them by the Matron of the Hospital.
3.   They must be between 21 and 48 years of age for Home Service, and 23 and 42 for Foreign Service.
4.   They will be required to live in quarters provided by the Nursing Staff of the Military Hospitals, under the control and supervision of the Matron.
5.   They will be required to adhere strictly to the Time Tables in force in the Military Hospitals, and to the Regulations and Standing Orders for the Services, so far as such orders concern them.
6.   They will wear the washing uniform of their detachments at all times when on duty.
7.   The Uniform Allowance of paid VAD nursing members employed in Military Hospitals will in future be issuable at the rate of £2 10s. 0d. half-yearly, instead of £2 as at present. The allowance will be issuable in

advance at the beginning of each six months' engagement (i.e. no allowance will be issuable in respect of the month's probationary service). The first issue of the increased rate will be made, in the case of ladies at present serving, from the first day of their next six months' of service. Any member breaking her engagement within six months of its commencement will be required to refund £1 5s. of the allowance.

8.    They will be appointed for one month on probation; at the expiration of this time, if recommended by the Matron for further service, they will be required to sign an agreement to serve for six months or the duration of the War, at home or abroad, as required. Their salary shall be at the rate of £20 per annum; and all probationers who, on completion of their current agreement, enter immediately on a subsequent term of six months' employment, are to be paid at the rate of £22 10s. per annum from the first day of the further term of employment. Probationers who sign an agreement to serve for so long as required will be eligible for further increment of £2 10s. each half year until they reach the maximum rate of £30 per annum, the first increment taking effect six months after the date on which they become entitled to £22 10s. per annum. Only continuous service will reckon toward this increment of pay, i.e., probationers who return to civil life within the completion of one period of service and the beginning of another will not be allowed to count any service given before their temporary return to civil life.

9.    The engagement of Voluntary Aid Detachment members will be terminated at any time if found unfit in any respect for service.

10.  Leave will be granted as follows – During the first six months = 7 days. During the second six months = 14 days. This will be taken as and when the exigencies of the service permit.

Travelling – A first class railway warrant is sent to nursing members proceeding to a Military Hospital.

In addition, the list of clothing and equipment (opposite), specified by the Red Cross as necessary for overseas work, indicated the spartan nature of their living arrangements and the limited nursing interventions that they were authorised to carry out.

In the opening months of the war the circumstances in which professional and volunteer nurses lived were not well thought out or properly planned. There were no special billeting arrangements for them and they slept and washed in a variety of venues – hotels, convents, schools, railway stations, sports stadiums, theatres, and sometimes the great outdoors, were used to house nurses on active service. Tents became the mainstay of their accommodation. The 'kit' of nurses embarking on overseas service was basic. One sister recounted the functional items as specified by the War Office:

Besides the usual uniform, there was camp equipment, comprising a

# List of Required Clothing and Equipment
(# - total, A – worn, B – in trunk, C – in handbag, D – in bread bag)

| | Item | # | A | B | C | D | Notes |
|---|---|---|---|---|---|---|---|
| 1 | Coat with unbuttonable collar or turn-down cloth | | | | | | |
| 2 | Hat, bonnet, or headcloth | | | | | | |
| 3 | Cap | | | | | | |
| 4 | Vest, cloth or knitted scarf | | | | | | In inclement seasons otherwise in trunk |
| 5 | Wash clothes | | | | | | |
| 6 | Wool dress | | | | | | |
| 7 | Collar or neckcloth | | | | | | |
| 8 | Aprons, white | | | | | | |
| 9 | Aprons, coloured | | | | | | |
| 10 | Night jackets | | | | | | Or night shirts |
| 11 | Shirts | | | | | | According to need |
| 12 | Wool undershirts | | | | | | To no. 14 & 16 or 3 bloomers |
| 13 | Corset or reform-corset | | | | | | |
| 14 | Petticoat | | | | | | |
| 15 | Dust-skirt | | | | | | |
| 16 | Trousers | | | | | | |
| 17 | Stockings | | | | | | |
| 18 | Leather laced boots, high | | | | | | |
| 19 | Leather shoes with double heels, pair | | | | | | |
| 20 | Shoes, warm, pair | | | | | | |
| 21 | Galoshes, pair | | | | | | |
| 22 | Handkerchiefs, pair | | | | | | |
| 23 | Gloves, pair | | | | | | |
| 24 | Umbrella | | | | | | |
| 25 | Toilette kit, incl. toothbrush, nail brush, comb | | | | | | |
| 26 | Hand-towel | | | | | | |
| 27 | Mirror, small | | | | | | |
| 28 | Clothes brush | | | | | | |
| 29 | Shoe cleaning kit | | | | | | |
| 30 | Sewing kit | | | | | | |
| 31 | Mending bag | | | | | | |
| 32 | Knife, fork, spoon; in a case | | | | | | |
| 33 | Drinking cup | | | | | | |
| 34 | Canteen | | | | | | |
| 35 | Pocket-knife | | | | | | |
| 36 | Pouch with writing implements | | | | | | |
| 37 | Change purse | | | | | | |
| 38 | Travel inkwell | | | | | | |
| 39 | Lantern | | | | | | |
| 40 | Lighter | | | | | | |
| 41 | Stearine candle for lantern | | | | | | |
| 42 | (Collapsible) Rubber basin | | | | | | |
| 43 | Military songbook (hymnal?) | | | | | | |
| 44 | New Testament with Psalms | | | | | | |
| 45 | Neutrality insignia | | | | | | |
| 46 | Identity card | | | | | | |
| 47 | Expenditure book | | | | | | |
| 48 | Bandages according to #75 | | | | | | |
| 49 | Bandage packets | | | | | | |
| 50 | Identity disk* | | | | | | * To be worn on a cord under clothing |
| 51 | Iron ration** | | | | | | ** When used |

folding bedstead, folding chair, folding washstand with basin, and a bath and bucket, these last four being of canvas and water proof; all these pack easily into the kit-bag. The other two things allowed are a trunk 32 by 14 by 24 in, and a hold-all. A pillow, a cushion, a mackintosh, knife, fork and spoon, tea-infuser, stove and kettle, flat-iron, two thermometers, two pairs scissors, two forceps, enamelled cup or mug, gum boots, a rug, soap, towels, fountain-pen (a thermos, too, if you like), are among the things mentioned as necessities. Armed with these, I felt ready for all the many exigencies of life in a tent.

One staff nurse posted to a military hospital at Rouen, and living in less than suitable accommodation, was quite philosophical about her situation:

I am still living, sleeping, feeding and working under canvas ... a fellow nurse from the same hospital back home shares a bell-tent with me, and if we sometimes wonder whether the next gust of wind will leave us homeless and roofless, we are now quite accustomed to dealing with such trifling accidents. One stormy night one of the large tents holding thirty patients was lifted bodily, and sailed away in the distance, leaving the occupants looking up at a stormy sky, a most amusing episode when we found that no one had been hurt.

We have now been given wooden floors to our tents, and so no longer have the pleasure of the company of the little worms at night. The weather has been appallingly cold, and the cases of acute frostbite from the trenches have been numerous.

**Nurses' accommodation at No 10 General Hospital. By the winter of 1915, nurses were billeted in huts, tents and any available accommodation in and around hospitals; some lived in casinos or sports stadiums.**

Perhaps the War Office had been silently praying that the war would be over by Christmas, saving time, money, and the need to engage effectively with the necessities of establishing working and living environments sympathetic to the needs of the sick and injured, and the women who nursed them. In the midst of the carnage and the debates about the deficiencies in the medical and nursing arrangements, unnoticed in the casualty lists was the name of Miss W. Bell, an eighteen year old 'nurse' who, it was claimed, 'died of her wounds in hospital'. According to reports, Miss Bell was 'attending the wounded in the firing-line when a shell smashed both her legs'. *The Nursing Times* wasted no time in condemning the situation and asked: 'Under whose auspices did Miss Bell go to France?' While there was a general appreciation of the 'imposing funeral' held by the French for the deceased nurse, *The Nursing Times* sceptically went on to state:

> We recognise the bravery of our countrywoman and heartily appreciate the desire of the French people to honour her mortal remains. But it is scandalous that a girl of eighteen, obviously untrained and inexperienced, should have been engaged in nursing in the firing-line; and whoever is responsible for such an outrage should be brought to book.

It is difficult to know if the tone of moral outrage expressed in *The Nursing Times* was due to the tragic and premature death of a young woman or because she was 'untrained and inexperienced'. This young woman's death afforded her the 'honour' of being the first nurse to lose her life while serving on the Western Front.

While the doctors and nurses on the Western Front were engaged in life and death struggles, there was a desperate shortage of hospital beds on the Home Front. The Territorial Hospitals had to increase the beds at most hospitals from 520 and nursing staff from 91 to the levels indicated in the table overleaf.

There was, however, no shortage of women diligently producing comfort supplies for the troops. According to a notice in the *British Journal of Nursing*, 300,000 woollen belts and socks were needed for the men of the BEF. Anyone wishing to contribute to the supplies was informed that instructions on how to make the articles of clothing could be obtained from the Lady-in-Waiting to the Queen at Devonshire House, Piccadilly, London. The making of comfort garments, and shirts was caricatured in a humorous tongue-twisting song entitled 'Sister Susie's Sewing Shirts for Soldiers'.

Sister Susie's Sewing Shirts for Soldiers
Sister Susie's sewing in the kitchen on a 'Singer'
There's miles and miles of flannel on the floor
And up the stairs,

And father says it's rotten getting mixed up with the cotton,
And sitting on the needles that she leaves upon the chairs…
Some soldiers send epistles
Say they'd sooner sleep on thistles
Than the saucy, soft, short shirts for soldiers sister Susie sews.

| Hospital | Place | Beds | Trained Staff | Untrained Staff |
|---|---|---|---|---|
| 1st London | Camberwell | 1,040 | 122 | 90 |
| 2nd London | Chelsea | 820 | 96 | 70 |
| 3rd London | Wandsworth | 950 | 111 | 82 |
| 4th London | Denmark Hill | 970 | 114 | 84 |
| 1st Southern | Birmingham | 3,210 | 375 | 280 |
| 2nd Southern | Bristol | 2,300 | 268 | 201 |
| 3rd Southern | Oxford | 1,008 | 118 | 87 |
| 4th Southern | Plymouth | 520 | 61 | 45 |
| 5th Southern | Portsmouth | 520 | 61 | 45 |
| 1st Eastern | Cambridge | 1,550 | 181 | 135 |
| 2nd Eastern | Brighton | 1,001 | 95 | 79 |
| 1st Western | Liverpool | 1,800 | 210 | 157 |
| 2nd Western | Manchester | 3,554 | 415 | 310 |
| 3rd Western | Cardiff | 1,910 | 223 | 166 |
| 1st Northern | Newcastle | 739 | 86 | 64 |
| 2nd Northern | Leeds | 1,900 | 222 | 165 |
| 3rd Northern | Sheffield | 1,750 | 204 | 153 |
| 4th Northern | Lincoln | 1,004 | 118 | 87 |
| 5th Northern | Leicester | 1,870 | 218 | 163 |
| 1st Scottish | Aberdeen | 1,180 | 118 | 102 |
| 2nd Scottish | Edinburgh | 900 | 105 | 78 |
| 3rd Scottish | Glasgow | 1,290 | 151 | 102 |
| 4th Scottish | Glasgow | 780 | 91 | 67 |
| | | 32,566 | 3,653 | 2,812 |

**The Territorial Hospitals had to increase the beds at most hospitals from 520 and nursing staff from 91 to the levels indicated in the table above.**

Such was the enthusiasm for making comfort garments, particularly socks, the War Office lobbied the government to do something about the over-supply. It was claimed that soldiers had the luxury of wearing a pair of socks once and then throw them away! Stock (sock) piling for leaner days was not an attractive option for the Government and War Office.

Clearly wishing to make a contribution, the Queen, in a gesture of *noblesse oblige*, sent a dress length of what was described as 'grey material' to a soldier's wife in each regiment of the 1st and 2nd Division at Aldershot saying, 'I wish them to feel that I am thinking of them in their great anxiety, and I admire their pluck.'

While the supply of socks, woollen belts and dress lengths had the support of royalty (and Sister Susie), Mrs Gunthorpe, a trained nurse, was enjoying a modest degree of fame with her new invention, the Helpless Shirt. The garment was designed to keep wounded soldiers warm and comfortable while minimising the aggravation of wounds. Through voluntary production of comfort garments, the women of Britain and Ireland were able to keep their minds and hands occupied, and their men comfortable. On the backs of the dead and the misfortunes of war, economic opportunism was just beginning. In the established garment industry an entrepreneurial spirit was alive and doing rather well; garments were being designed and manufactured under the heading 'Fashionable Mourning Clothes'.

Selfridges, which opened on Oxford Street in 1909 and was hailed as the first great 'superstore', was doing its bit for the war effort and making money in the process. The management allowed a Red Cross Depot to be opened on the ground floor of the store, claiming that it was established to:

> ... supply everything required by ladies working for the British Red Cross Society or Nursing Associations. Purchasers of material will be supplied free with copies of the official garment patterns. Every assistance will gladly be given to ladies organising Nursing Corps or equipping private hospitals.

Furthermore, the men of the regular army, the territorials and volunteers were invited to attend the 'studio' on the first floor of the new men's store at Marble Arch where they could have for free, 'three copies of their photograph in uniform'.

While the main focus of charitable works and public-giving was aimed at the comfort of troops, the care of animals engaged in war work was attracting a fair amount of sympathy. In a letter to the *Daily Mirror*, Ethel Bilborough wrote of her concerns for the horses that were being sent off to war.

> I chanced to be at Waterloo Station when several fine horses were patiently waiting to be taken off to war, and the thought struck me how infinitely sad it is to contemplate the terrible pain that these poor creatures may be called upon to bear when left to die slowly, and in torment on the battlefield. Can no one suggest means whereby these suffering animals could be mercifully put out of their misery at the end of an encounter?

Miss Bilborough was not alone; nurses on active service were claiming it was distressful enough caring for the human casualties of war without the added emotional strain of tending to abandoned, sick or injured animals. Gertrude Holland who was attached to a hospital in Antwerp explained the strength of emotion she felt for abandoned animals and the action she took to relieve them of their suffering:

My heart bled at the pathetic sight of the many dogs and cats that refused to leave the piles of what had been their homes. Many of these were mad with starvation and snarled when we approached them. It seemed so terrible that these faithful dumb pets of scattered families should also have to suffer in such an awful way.

The next day I returned, borrowed a rifle from a soldier, and another soldier and myself went round shooting these miserable howling and starving things. I saw a small kitten, frightened by our firing, rush out of the remains of a house, and I was just about to shoot it when it ran towards me and sat at my feet. I hate cats, but the poor wee thing looked so pathetic as it looked up at me with its little mouth open, that I stopped and picked it up, and it was then I saw that it had but three feet, one of its back ones having been shot off and the stump was bleeding. I carried it to the hospital and dressed its wound. It went back to Antwerp with us as the mascot of our hospital.

The Royal Society for the Prevention of Cruelty to Animals (RSPCA), following protracted negotiations with the Army Council, finally received official sanction to assist the Army Veterinary Corps with the care and welfare of sick and injured animals. At the beginning of the war, the RSPCA had offered its services to the War Office, but the War Office rejected their expertise as it did many other valuable services. The War Office had become as famous for its rejection of volunteer services as its reputed failure to deliver the established services it had commissioned.

At the start of the war, the Blue Cross Fund was launched by Our Dumb Friends' League, a society formed, it was claimed, for the 'encouragement of kindness to animals'. The money raised by the Blue Cross went towards the care of military horses and it supported the work of the authorised veterinary service by supplying hospitals, ambulances and suppliers. In addition to the Blue Cross Fund, through the auspices of the RSPCA, the Duke of Portland chaired a special council that organised funds for animal welfare.

While there was genuine concern about the vulnerability of animals, there was also some concern that innocent members of the public could be subject to deception. Reports in the national and nursing press highlighted two incidents, both involving the word 'nurse'. The Manchester Stipendiary Magistrate sentenced a young woman to three months in jail for obtaining food and lodgings by deception. Apparently she fooled her landladies into believing that she was a nurse who was attending the local hospital for treatment to 'the sinews of her left arm having been cut by the Germans'. The story was a hoax and the young lady went to prison with her arm intact, but not her reputation. In Scotland, a seventeen year old girl attracted a lot of public sympathy and press attention after claiming that her elder sister had gone to Belgium to work as a nurse and was subsequently captured by

Germans. She further claimed that the Germans had murdered her sister but, before doing so, had cut off her breasts. The story was the product of an over fertile imagination and a complete fabrication. Clearly, both women took advantage of the public esteem in which wartime nurses were held and the Belgian atrocity stories which, in the opening months of the war, were regularly featured in the press, propaganda leaflets and posters.

A letter to the Editor of the *British Journal of Nursing* from a nurse from Prestwick highlighted the need for accurate reporting.

Dear Madam

In the *British Journal of Nursing*, October 24th, reference is made to something that is happening behind the walls of the English Navy. The English Navy! – May one be allowed to ask what is the English Navy and to state that no such Navy has existed for hundreds of years ... The Navy which is doing such splendid work just now, defending Britain and British Trade, is the British Navy not the English Navy, and belongs to the whole of Britain and Ireland; the vessels comprising it and their crews also hailing from different parts of the Kingdom. As for the Army – so slightingly alluded to in the press as English; several of its most famous regiments belong to Scotland and Ireland.

That being so it is nothing short of cruelty to ignore those brave men of the sister countries who are giving their lives so freely on sea and land to maintain the integrity of the British Empire.

Had England been allowed to absorb the other countries it would have been different, but each has its own name in the Union and on the map, and it is more than time than the southern portion of the Kingdom realised that she is a part of that Kingdom and can never be other until the Union is dissolved.

It was understandable that the misuse of 'English' left the nurse aggrieved as, regrettably, in the opening months of the war, 5,046 men died serving in the Scottish Regiments of the British Army. The Irish, who had a long tradition of volunteering their services to the Crown, sustained 2,161 deaths in the Irish Regiments, and during the same period, the Welsh Regiments lost 1,147 men. The figures did not include the deaths of Scottish, Irish and Welsh men serving in all other sections and corps of the British Army. While the nurse fulminated about inaccurate terminology, Sir George McCrae, in Edinburgh, was using his oratorical skills to encourage young Scottish men to enlist in the British Army. On 27 November, in the newly completed Usher Hall, built for the people of Edinburgh by the family of Millicent Peterkin, Sir George made an emotional speech and plea to the thousands of men assembled in the hall.

I stand before you humbly as a fellow Scot, nothing more nothing less.

You know I don't speak easily of crisis. But that is what confronts us. I have received permission from the War Office to raise a new battalion for active service. It is my intention that this unit will be characterised by such a spirit of simple excellence that the rest of Lord Kitchener's army will be judged by our standard. Furthermore, with the agreement of the authorities, I have undertaken to lead the battalion in the field. I would not – I could not ask you to serve if I did not share the danger at your side. In a moment I will walk down Castle Street and set my name to the list of volunteers. Who will join me?

Many men felt compelled to enlist because of the pressures that women, and not recruiting officers, brought to bear on them. Clearly divorced from the realities and consequences of war, The Women's Service League, in a vulgar display of emotional blackmail, produced a press petition urging women to shame men into volunteering for war service:

> At this hour of grave peril and desperate need I do hereby pledge myself most solemnly in the name of my King and country to persuade every man I know to offer his services to his country ... I also pledge myself never to be seen in public with any man who, being in every way fit and free for service, has refused to respond to his country's call.

While recruiting speeches, press adverts and petitions were heavily laced with emotion or emotional blackmail, an Editorial in the *British Journal of Nursing*, entitled 'Emotional Nursing,' returned to the theme of untrained nurses serving on the Western Front.

> The wide-spread desire to do something to alleviate the suffering of the sick and wounded at the present time is one with which all must sympathise, but it is also one which must be directed into the proper channels, lest it not only fail in its intention, but even aggravates instead of alleviates suffering. The first impulse of many women is to go to the front where the front is they have often only the vaguest notion ... before acting on that impulse it is imperative that they should consider what qualifications they have for being of use, for, in the stern work of war only those who are of use are acceptable, others are not only not wanted, but hinder and hamper the genuine worker.'

Needless to say, no evidence was offered for the alleged poor quality of nursing, or the fact that volunteer nurses were not wanted. For once, perhaps, the usual criticism of untrained nurses that had become commonplace in the professional nursing journals was probably justified. Furthermore, trained nurses were beginning to sense that powerful influences were shaping the policy for nursing standards and services. The Editorial went on to observe:

The medical profession in wartime is happily free from invasion by incompetent amateurs. It is organised, protected and certain minimum standards are maintained by law, but, in connection with nursing, there is no similar organisation, and the result is that to many with a desire to help the sick and wounded, especially the wounded, the simplest way appears to be to proceed to the seat of war to nurse them, and if money and influence can accomplish this, forthwith they go.

Money and influence may have bought a place at the front but, as the trained nurses would attest, it could not buy skill or the physical and mental stamina needed to cope with the casualties of war. By November 1914, in addition to the eighteen-year-old Miss Bell, who died tragically in France, four more nurses had died in service: three staff nurses and one nursing sister.

In spite of the day-to-day privations, the emotional and physical strain of caring for the sick and wounded, and the loss of life amongst the troops and her colleagues, one Sister remained optimistic. As the first Christmas of the war approached, she was still able to claim:

It seems strange that Christmas will soon be here. We shall think of you all, and if we feel a little homesick I suppose it cannot be wondered at. What do an armchair, a warm fire, and a hot bath feel like? We often wonder when we tub in our little square of canvas. But we are quite, quite happy, and never regret coming out.

The *Daily Express* which had been collecting money for the 'Nurses' Presents' Fund announced that, thanks to the generosity of the public, it now had a sufficient sum to buy a Christmas present for every British nurse serving at the front. Each nurse would receive a small white leather case which would be compact enough to fold over and place in a pocket. The front of the case would have a gold embossed crown and four flags, with the words 'Christmas 1914' and printed on the inside flap it would say, 'From the readers of the *Daily Express*'. The gift was designed to 'convey to the heroines of the nursing line in France and Flanders the Yuletide greetings and deep gratitude of the people at home'.

The war was giving rise to considerable philanthropy and public-giving and as the Christmas season arrived, so did the news that, thanks to the beneficence of anonymous donors, every soldier would now carry an ampoule of iodine in his field dressing pack, thus minimising the chance of wound infection. Arrangements were made to support the men who would be spending their first or for many, tragically, their last Christmas in a war hospital. Princess Mary appealed to the nation:

**A Queen Alexandra's Imperial Military Nursing Service sister looking out over the deck of HMHS *Neuralia* where a contingent of Royal Army Medical Corps men are waiting to have their photograph taken.**

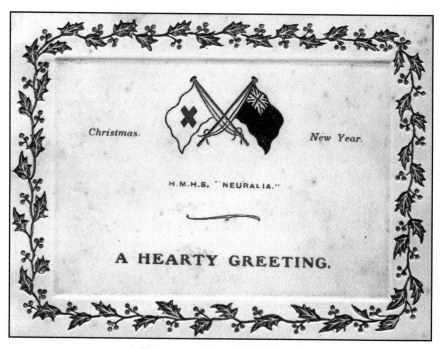

**A Christmas card from HMHS *Neuralia***

Help me to send a Christmas present from the whole of the nation to every sailor afloat and every soldier at the front. I am sure we would all be happier to feel that we had helped to send our little token of love and sympathy on Christmas morning, something that would be useful and of permanent value, and the making of which may be a means of providing employment in trades adversely affected by the war. Could there be anything more likely to hearten them in their struggle than a present received straight from home on Christmas Day?

Please will you help me?'

The Princess Mary Sailors' and Soldiers' Christmas Fund was established, and the gifts the men received from a grateful nation were pipe tobacco and pipe, twenty cigarettes, a tinder lighter, a Christmas card and a photograph of the Princess; they were enclosed in a small brass box. Alternative boxes were designed for non-smokers.

Callard and Bowser sent toffee and Cadburys dispatched chocolate to the front. Not to be outdone by the *Daily Express*, the *Daily Mail* sent plumb puddings; each man would receive a quarter of a pound as his Christmas treat. On the Western Front on Christmas Eve, Sister Peterkin set about organising Christmas food and gifts for her patients and the hospital orderlies.

Sister O'Conner and I went into town this afternoon to do our Christmas shopping, in the way of getting eatables for the men's tea on Christmas Day. Everyone else seemed to be on the same errand... Have spent all evening making up little packets for each man tomorrow... We are giving each patient 3 white handkerchiefs, a cake of scented soap, a packet of chocolate or butterscotch, and half a dozen packets of Woodbines. To each of our six orderlies we are giving a warm vest, a muffin, a pair of socks, a pair of mittens, three handkerchiefs, notepaper, envelopes, and postcards (half a dozen of each), pencil, a packet of toffee, six packets of Woodbines, two packets of Three Castles cigarettes, a box of matches, and a little card of good wishes. Quite a nice parcel. Sister O'Conner has gone to midnight Mass.

According to Sister Peterkin, Christmas had been a very full, active and happy Day for the soldiers and nursing staff.

Christmas Day! And what a change from last year. In spite of everything, the men have thoroughly enjoyed themselves. The Sisters and Medical Officers of No. 10 Hospital came round singing carols last night, which were much appreciated. There were Church services at 6.30 and 7.15 this morning. The tents have all been more or less decorated, and some are really very pretty. At dinner time everyone had soup, an ordinary diet (meat), and a bottle of stout, followed by plum pudding and brandy sauce.

We made the sauce in the wards the night before. Each tent had a fine tea party, with plenty of cakes, biscuits, sweets, and fruit and our men also had tinned salmon, which is a thing that Tommy loves. The men spent a most hilarious evening, sitting round their stoves, roasting chestnuts, eating apples and oranges, and singing and joking to their heart's content. During the day each man received a card from the King and Queen, and Princess Mary's gift, with both of which they were delighted, and also a little packet of tobacco, sweets, etc., from the Red Cross Society ... We Sisters had a fine dinner in the evening, with all sorts of fruits, nuts, wines, and crackers to finish off with ... After dinner we went out carol singing, and made rather a picturesque procession.

I think it was moonlight, but foggy, owing to the keen frost, and everyone was in a long coat, with white caps (some still wearing their paper hats as well), and most of us carrying lanterns. We went all round our own Hospital, then went down to No. 10, and marched up the road, and visited No. 11 Stationary Hospital, to which the Scottish Red Cross Hospital is attached. The Officers there kindly asked us into their cosy mess room, and treated us to wine, cake, and the gramophone! They were all very jolly, and we quite enjoyed our visit. Matron is really very sporting! We got back to our own quarters about midnight, and marched in great spirits, singing such ditties as 'Tipperary', 'Here We Are Again' and 'We Won't Be Home Till Morning'!'

**Royal Army Medical Corps doctors, and Queen Alexandra's Imperial Military Nursing Service nurses celebrating Christmas. Like everyone else they believed the war would be 'over by Christmas'.**

There was no respite for Sister Luard who was dealing with the casualties of war on a Hospital Train. From Christmas Eve until Boxing Day, she highlighted the tragic, comical, liberal and at times surreal situations in which she and other nurses found themselves.

Christmas Eve. Just nearing Boulogne with another bad load, half Indian, half British … Headquarters had to be evacuated after the Germans got through on Sunday. The two regiments, Coldstream Guards and Camerons, who drove them back, lost heavily and tell a tragic story. There are two men (only one is a boy) on the train that got wounded on Monday night (both compound fracture of the thigh) and were only taken out of the trench this morning, (Thursday), to a Dressing Station and then straight on to our train. Why they are alive I don't know, but I'm afraid they won't live long: they are sunken and grey-faced and just strong enough to say, 'Anyway, I'm out of the trench now.' They had drinks of water now and then in the field but no dressings, and lay in the slush. Stretcher-bearers are shot down immediately, with or without the wounded, by the German snipers. And this is Christmas, and the world is supposed to be civilised.

They came in from the trenches to-day with blue faces and chattering teeth, and it was all one could do to get them warm and fed. By this evening they were most of them revived enough to enjoy Xmas cards; there were such a nice lot that they were able to choose them to send to Mother and My Young Lady and the Missis and the Children, and have one for themselves. The Indians each had one, and salaamed and said, 'God save you,' and 'I will pray to God for you,' and 'God win your enemies,' and 'God kill many Germans,' and 'The Indian men too cold, kill more Germans if not too cold.' One with a South African ribbon spotted mine and said, 'Africa same like you … With superhuman self-control I have not opened my mail tonight so as to have it tomorrow morning.

Xmas Day – A howling mob of reinforcements stormed the train for smokes. We threw out every cigarette, pipe, pair of socks, mits, hankies, pencils we had left; it was like feeding chickens, but of course we hadn't nearly enough …

Every one on the train has had a card from the King and Queen in a special envelope with the Royal Arms in red on it. And this is the message (in writing hand) –
'With our best wishes for Christmas, 1914.
May God protect you and bring you home safe.
MARY R. GEORGE R.I.'
That is something to keep, isn't it?

This is a very slow journey up, with long indefinite stops; we all got bad headaches by lunch time from the intense cold. At lunch we had hot bricks for our feet, and hot food inside, which improved matters, The orderlies are to have their Xmas dinner tomorrow, but I believe ours is to be tonight, if the patients are settled up in time ...

7 P.M. We may have to fill up at Hazebrouck, which will interrupt the very festive Xmas dinner the French Staff are getting ready for us. It takes a man, French or British, to take decorating really seriously. The orderlies have done wonders with theirs, aeroplanes done in cotton-wool on brown blankets is one feature.

12 Midnight – Had a very festive Xmas dinner, soup, turkey, peas, mince pies, plum pudding, chocolate, champagne, absinthe, and coffee. Absinthe is delicious, like squills. We had many toasts in French and English. We got up and clinked glasses with the French Staff at every toast, and finally the little chef came in and sang to us in a very sweet musical tenor. Our great anxiety is to get as many orderlies and NCOs as possible through the day without being run in for drunk, but it is an uphill job; I don't know where they get it.

Saturday, December 26th – saw my lambs off the train before breakfast. One man in the Warwicks had twelve years' service, a wife and two children, but 'when Kitchener wanted more men' he rejoined. This week he got an explosive bullet through his arm, smashing it up to rags above the elbow ... The V.A.D. here brought a present to every man on the train this morning, and to the orderlies. They had 25,000 to distribute, cigarette cases, writing cases, books, pouches, &c. The men were frightfully pleased, it was so unexpected.

6 P.M. – We all processed to the Orderlies' Mess truck and the O.C. made a speech ... He had to propose 'The Sisters,' and after a few trembling, solemn words about 'we all know the good work they do' he suddenly giggled hopelessly, and it ended in a healthy splodge all round ... The men [orderlies] are just now so merry with singing 'Tipperary', and dressing up, that they will surely drop the patients off the stretchers, but we'll hope for the best.

For the men in the trenches or the billets behind the front line, Christmas was not quite so comfortable or festive. Robert Scott Mcfie was a Colour Quartermaster Sergeant in the 10th King's Liverpool Regiment, known as the Liverpool Scottish. In a letter to his sister written on Christmas Eve he explained the sentiments of the men and the environment in which they were about to spend Christmas.

This is Christmas Eve, and we are all very home sick. The men are in an empty barn cold and draughty, and have scarcely recovered from our spell in the trenches … 94 of the company we brought out from England remain, and it is evident that we have almost ceased to exist as a regiment. The men are singing in the barn to keep up their spirits … we are waiting to march off to an even less comfortable residence in which to spend Xmas, viz. dugouts holes in the ground, cheaply roofed and furnished with straw.'

As it happened, Mcfie and his men did not spend Christmas Day in the trenches; instead they were sent to billets in a cold barn near 'an odd straggling village, almost every house in which, as seems usual here, is an inn or café'.

On Christmas Day, an unofficial truce took place in different parts of the line. A strange mixture of curiosity and humanity had brought together soldiers from the opposing armies. The spirit of Christmas appeared to be stronger than the will to kill. The truce saw the belligerents shaking hands, exchanging souvenirs, food and drink, and engaging in 'friendly' football matches. Both sides sang Christmas carols and popular songs. In the casualty clearing stations and base hospitals, doctors, nurses, orderlies, sick and wounded soldiers celebrated Christmas in a spirit of good faith and sang their carols with optimism. In reality, it would be quite some time before there was 'Peace on Earth and Goodwill towards Men.' During Christmas week, Captain Barnett of the Royal Army Medical Corps made a depressing prediction: 'I think we will win through, but our casualties will be appalling.' He was right, Armageddon had only just begun.

Chapter V

## *'Oh What a Lovely War'*

# Living, Fighting, Dying and Nursing 1915

For the officers of the 2nd battalion The Royal Welch Fusiliers, 1915 began inauspiciously. On New Year's Day, the cook managed to confuse the Officers' Mess dinner arrangements by sending the brandy butter with the turkey, and bread sauce with the plum pudding. On the same day, a draft of ninety other ranks was 'welcomed' into the battalion. Working in a ninety-bed hospital near the front line, a fellow countrywoman, Sister Grace Hughes, had more than culinary protocols occupying her mind, hands and time. From a wealth of hard-earned knowledge and experience, Sister Hughes well knew it would only be a matter of time before at least one third of the new draft would be affected by sickness, injury or, quite often, both. Commenting with optimism and compassion on the recent casualty admissions to her hospital, she claimed:

> We have some marvellous recoveries, and now are working hard to save many other seriously wounded patients. In no case, however, as yet, has the most up-to-date treatment for tetanus availed. One English boy died from tetanus last week, such a nice Yorkshire lad of nineteen. He also had lost a limb, and had pneumonia on entry. Three of our nurses have had to give up through ill health, but the place suits me very well, and I am quite fit every day. It is a sight beyond words to see the stretchers arriving; I often have to choke back the tears. One morning while I was dressing the face of a Belgian sergeant, whose dauntless pluck quite upset me, I had to go into the next room until I could come back with dry eyes. His face and chin and most of his tongue had been shot away ... The plight of the men on admission is beyond description. Ice-cold feet, socks sodden and like paper, and stuck to their feet; clothes all gore and mud dried in for many days, and many suffering from gangrene, peritonitis, fractures of all sorts, and injuries in some cases from head to foot. One had both legs and hands off. The bladder and head cases are almost the worst. It would take too

long to tell you of our visits to the station shed where six or seven hundred wounded, of all nationalities, lie on straw and stretchers.

The on-going experiences of this cruel war provided the New Year welcome to Sister Hughes, the officers and men of the Royal Welch Fusiliers, and everyone serving on the Western Front.

At the beginning of the year, the BEF was in no condition to take part in prolonged offensive action as most of its skilled fighting force was lost in the 1914 battles. Tragically, the men of the old regular army were by now all but gone. According to *Punch,* the pessimists were 'having a fine time' after the Under-Secretary of War claimed that 'the army costs more in a week than the total estimates for the Waterloo campaign, and our casualties on the Western Front have amounted to over 100,000.' In addition to the loss of well-trained men, the War Office again displayed its penchant for skilled intransigence by dragging its feet over the supply of ordnance, particularly high explosives. In spite of continued requests by senior army officers, ammunition and guns failed to materialise. According to David Lloyd George, who was the Minister for Munitions:

> The old six-inch howitzers which had arrived just in time for the battle of the Aisne in 1914 did not secure for the army the numbers that were needed by the end of January 1915 ... only 24 of these weapons in the field – one sixteenth the numbers that were being used against us by the Germans.

Describing the philosophy at the War Office as 'traditional reactionism', he observed that its policy 'seemed ever to be that of preparing, not for the next war, but for the last one or the last but one' and that the problems of 'shortage, delays, misfits and muddles' lay in their hands. At this point of the war, all that the BEF could hope for was to hold the ground it had gained and to look to the ebullience of Kitchener's volunteers to determine its course and outcome.

Not all volunteers carried arms. One retired Army nursing sister, having decided that she was still fit and able to contribute to the care of the sick and wounded, volunteered her services for the war effort. On her way to a Red Cross Hospital in France she was detailed to nurse wounded French soldiers and came upon a group of British soldiers at a French railway station.

> I was soon in the midst of a group of them, and I told them that I too had served in the army. They just let themselves go, and how they talked! A little Argyll and Sutherland Highlander and a small man in the Royal Irish on either side of me, each tried to see how long he could hold the floor, and when they paused for a moment a man in the Scots Greys at the back

hurled forth information, and a quiet boy in the Middlesex, minus all his badges, spoke when he got the chance. These men were all in the fighting at Mons and Le Cateau, and told me cheerfully of incidents, only sobering down for a moment when they spoke of the retreat, which they said was awful. I was struck by the way they talked of their officers, saying there never was (*sic*) such men. These men were on their way to a rest camp before returning to the Front.

By January 1915, the Front had become synonymous with harsh conditions; the men were not only fighting the enemy but also battling against the environment. The first winter of the war was extremely severe and the men described the living and fighting conditions in the trenches as 'dreadful'. One commentator likened life in the trenches to 'four million or more men living like human moles – from the North Sea to Switzerland there were three to four thousand miles of excavated earthworks.'

In diary entries between 3 and 8 January, James Jack, the Commanding Officer of 'C' Company, the Cameronians (Scottish Rifles), described the winter conditions in the trenches.

January 3rd: The rain is terrible. Much of the parapet is subsiding; sections of the trenches are nearly thigh-deep in water, and we can scarcely drag our legs through the mud when visiting the lines.

January 5th: The Prussian trenches, one or two hundred yards from ours, must also be flooded as we are delighted to see buckets of water being thrown over the parapet.

January 6th: Frankie Rooke was badly wounded this morning by a bullet in the groin. With just a field dressing bandaged on by the company stretcher-bearers, he had to lie in our shelter all day in considerable pain until he could be carried back safely at dusk to the ambulance …The men are great-hearted fellows. Their legs, capes and jerkins are habitually sodden with wet clay. Where there is a small patch of fairly solid ground the lucky ones off duty huddle round a coke brazier, of which each company has five. In spite of extremely long hours on duty in great discomfort, hard labour repairing our parapets and other defences, besides no proper meals in the trenches, there is little grumbling and never a whine from their lips whatever they may think of the business in hand.

January 7th: It is raining hard and the trenches are in an indescribable state, necessitating our having to be dragged out of bogs at times when on rounds. The enemy appear to be in a similar way, to judge by their bailing. The parapets have fallen dangerously low, and the men are confined to their posts which are like islands in a morass.

January 8th: The 8th was another miserable wet day in the trenches. That night the battalion, on relief by the 2nd Royal Welch Fusiliers, marched three and a half miles to billets in L'Armée two miles south of Armentières.

The officers of the 2nd Royal Welch evidently got over the confusion of their New Year's Day dinner and were once again preparing themselves for the hardships of the trenches. Moving up the line to relieve the Cameronians, an officer from the 2nd RWF observed that, 'The Cameronians had just lived in water.' Life was no better for the Royal Welch, and one officer found solace in the fact that 'Brother Boche was in the same pickle.'

Exposure to cold, wet and damp conditions produced illnesses such as bronchitis, pneumonia, dysentery, nephritis, boils and eczema. They were also afflicted by trench foot and frostbite. Frostbite was caused by exposing the body to sub-freezing temperatures. This was aggravated by wind or sweat, by drenching from rain and snow, or immersion in waterlogged trenches, subsequently causing damage to the skin, muscle, bone, blood vessels and nerve fibres. It only required a 45 minute exposure for fingers, toes, nose, earlobes and face to be affected; in severe cases it caused gangrene to limbs, nose and ears.

Trench foot was an extremely debilitating and painful condition. It was characterised by cold, swollen, pale feet, and men would claim their feet felt numb or like lead weights. As toe and ankle joints became stiff, walking and standing became very painful. The condition could result from long, quick marches to the trenches where men would arrive with hot and swollen feet, but prolonged exposure to waterlogged or frozen conditions was the major contributing factor. Defective or badly fitting footwear and constriction of the circulation by tightly fitting socks or puttees added to the problem. Infection and gangrene could set in when the condition was untreated. Contracting trench foot or frostbite became a military misdemeanour, and many senior officers were unsympathetic, blaming the men for carelessness or regarding it as a self-inflicted wound.

The environment in which men fought was determined by weather conditions which could not be controlled. In a letter home, an officer from the Royal Artillery wrote:

We stand to arms in the grey hours of the morning and watch the sun rising blood red over the German trenches, while we stamp our feet on the frozen ground to try to get warm after being up working half the night and spending the other half in a chilly dug-out, wondering whether our feet were made of us or of lead.

Initially, the army medical services were slow to respond to the identification and treatment of the condition and they spent the winter months experimenting with different forms of prevention such as putting rum in boots: this preventative measure was never adequately explained. In all probability, if rum had been given to the men to drink, it would have been psychologically better for easing their pain and discomfort. Distributing drink for therapeutic reasons certainly would not have received the blessing of Sir Victor Horsley who had managed to raise the hackles of many doctors by suggesting that the rum ration, already a feature of army and navy life, should be discontinued.

The doctor who accused Sir Victor in the columns of the *British Medical Journal* of having the intolerance of a teetotaller probably expressed the sentiments of many:

> If the soldier welcomes the anticipation and realisation of the rum ration, despite all real or assumed disadvantages, surely he is entitled to some say in the optional matter. Our army doctors have unique opportunities of judging its good or ill effects. It is unlikely that they would countenance its use if they thought it was really injurious. I think Sir Victor Horsley would do well to subordinate his teetotal principles to a calm consideration of the feelings of the men … Imagine the feelings of a Tommy if he was told that the rum ration must cease, not because army doctors and doctors generally disapproved of it, but because Sir Victor Horsley and his brother faddists differed from the majority. I think the answer would be 'Who is doing the fighting?'

Alcohol in army boots was only one recommendation. It was also suggested that the men should wrap their wet or frozen feet in cotton wool or flannel and re-warm them by the side of coke braziers. Exposure to direct heat was fraught with problems as it meant that the men could not judge the intensity of heat on numb feet, legs and hands. This 'solution' could lead to serious burns, and rapid re-warming had a detrimental effect on circulation and skin tissue. However, according to a nurse who was nursing the wounded at Aix le Bains:

> Many of my patients have frost bitten feet which are treated by hot air; this method is also employed with great success for slow healing superficial wounds.

Writing in the *British Medical Journal*, Dr Charles Davis explained to his colleagues that he had been 'entirely successful' with his treatment regime for frost bite of the feet.

> The best remedy I have found to be is a mixture of carron oil and cocaine. A small quantity is rubbed into the feet twice daily, special attention being

given to the toes; the feet are massaged with it for a few moments, and afterwards wrapped up in cotton wool.

Another advantage of Dr Davis's remedy was that his treatment allowed patients to sleep without narcotics being prescribed, which meant 'the men can more quickly be put on the convalescent list, thereby enabling them to get back sooner to the front.' Clearly, the doctor was helping to accommodate the War Office philosophy of winning the war with a minimum expenditure of time, men, material and money.

The war correspondent, Philip Gibbs, described what he saw as the cause of trench foot and the effect it had on the health of the troops.

> Men standing in slime for days and nights in field boots or puttees lost all sense of feeling in their feet. These feet of theirs, so cold and wet, began to swell, and go 'dead' and then suddenly to burn as though touched by red-hot pokers. Scores of men could not walk back from the trenches, but had to crawl, or be carried pick-a-back by their comrades. I saw hundreds of them, and as the winter dragged on, thousands.

In a mundane understatement, one soldier spoke for many when he said, 'We all wanted something more exciting than mud and water,' while Captain Frank Watson cynically observed that when trench foot appeared in his Division, someone conceived the idea that 'it was due to want of exercise, and could be cured by imposing more labour on men worn out by overwork, exposure, and want of sleep.'

It was not until January 1915 that, under Army Routine Order 554, a regime was initiated for the prevention of trench foot, consisting of a recommended combination of procedures such as wiping army boots inside and out with whale oil, regular washing of feet and massaging them with grease or oil and, finally, a regular application of clean, dry socks. Captain Watson supported the regime and successfully reduced the condition 'by the aid of dry socks sent up nightly with the rations'. It was just as well that, in spite of the War Office's discouragement, women were continuing to knit thousands of socks on the Home Front. Perhaps if army commanders had been more efficient in planning their manpower and supplies, and more sensitive to the health implications of men living in flooded and frozen trenches, trench foot could have been minimised. A better relief system for strained, exhausted and environmentally exposed troops and the supply of well-fitting socks and boots would have greatly reduced the pain and suffering of the 30,000 men affected by frostbite or trench foot during the first two years of the war.

While harsh weather conditions had serious implications for the men, their health was further compromised by sleep deprivation, body lice, fleas and rat infestations of trenches and dugouts. Private Clifford Lane of the 1st Battalion

**Number 10 General Hospital, Rouen, in the winter of 1915.**

Hertfordshire Regiment summed up the continual problem the troops suffered through sharing their trenches and dugouts with unwanted guests.

> Every man in the front line had fleas after about two or three weeks ... I've seen men taking their shirts off with the skin on their backs absolutely raw where they'd been scratching. And there was no way of getting rid of them at all ... Lice were a curse, were a real menace to us. For one thing, you had very few chances of getting a good sleep ... they drove you into a sort of frenzy almost.

Killing the rats was not an option as Fusilier Victor Packer of the Royal Irish Fusiliers explains:

> You would not kill rats because you had no means of getting rid of them. They would putrefy and it would be worse than if you left them alive. I think they lived in corpses, because they were huge, they were as big as cats, I am not exaggerating.

When soldiers claimed that the rats frequenting the trenches were as big as cats, they knew people back home would not believe them. To prove the point, men from the London Irish Regiment caught a rat, killed it, had it stuffed and then mounted. They brought their trophy back to London and, after much public viewing, it ended up in the Sergeants Mess of the Duke of York's Barracks, Chelsea.

While disease claimed lives, artillery appeared to be responsible for 60% of the traumatic deaths on the Western Front, which it was claimed, 'destroyed the mind and body of the front line'. High explosive shells were designed to break fortified enemy entrenchments and the wounding and maiming effects were obscene. When a shell exploded, it could carry earth, wood, corrugated iron, sandbags, barbed wire, and men into the air. Exploding shells could cost a man his sight or penetrate an abdomen, chest or head. They caused traumatic amputation of limbs and fractures to the skull, ribs and long bones. Shell blasts at close quarters caused concussion, nosebleed, vertigo, collapsed lungs and ruptures to the heart, kidneys, spleen, small bowel and eardrums. Shrapnel shells, invented in 1784 by Lieutenant Henry Shrapnel of the Royal Artillery, were designed to disperse hundreds of metal projectiles directly above, or in front of the opposing army's front line, ripping and tearing apart anything in their way. The damage that shells could inflict on the human anatomy was graphically described by the French soldier-novelist Henri Barbusse.

> Men squashed, cut in two, or divided from top to bottom, blown into showers by an ordinary shell, bellies turned inside out and scattered anyhow, skulls forced bodily into the chest as if blown with a club.

Believing that shells exploding at close quarters could concuss men's brains, enthusiastic and rather naïve psychiatrists diagnosed shell-shock in those men who no longer could tolerate the strain of war.

The sentiments of many troops serving on the Western front were summed up by Infantryman Wallace Lyon when he wrote:

> If a soldier is well fed, kept clear of lice and with constant attention to feet and clothing, he can stand a remarkable degree of cold and still remain healthy. It was the dreariness of being among the rats, the stench of death, the dirt, and the unceasing drain of casualties that told most on the troops' morale.

There were hundreds of conditions and injuries from which a man could die. Shell or sniper fire, could lead to instant death. If an injury led to uncontrolled haemorrhaging, the end would come quickly – in ten minutes or less. For those left in No Man's Land, without an immediate chance of rescue by stretcher-bearers or comrades, death could be slow and painful. If casualties survived the battlefield, they could later die in Casualty Clearing Stations or Base Hospitals with injury-related septicaemia and organ failure. Some war-acquired medical conditions such as tuberculosis, valvular disease of the heart and kidney failure led to severe debilitation and protracted death, and there were men who escaped physical injury only to spend the rest of their lives haunted by their war experiences. Many were not only mentally locked into their experiences but physically locked up, condemned to an asylum existence some described as a 'slow death.'

Human misery and loss of life and limb led to little progress in 1915. In spite of the continuous fighting, there was complete stagnation of movement. The most fluid situation of the Western Front was the endless transportation of men and materials up to the front line, followed by the daily evacuation of casualties.

Superstitions were rife as men watched the constant procession of sick and injured being moved to Casualty Clearing Stations and Base Hospitals. Some began to gamble on their odds of surviving the war. The writer and war correspondent, Michael MacDonagh, commented on the psychology of lucky charms and the power religious artefacts were having on serving soldiers.

> Since the outbreak of war there has been an extraordinary revival of the secular beliefs in omens, witchcraft, incantations and all that they imply – the direct influence of supernatural powers, of some sort or other, on the fortunes of individuals in certain events. The Army has returned to its old faith in the talisman.

The declining situation on the Western Front ensured that help, no matter where it came from, was more than welcome. Religious superstition saw non-Catholic soldiers emulating their Catholic comrades by wearing rosary beads around their necks or twisting the beads around the barrels of their guns. Father McCrory, the Connaught Rangers chaplain, graphically described injured men seeking solace in their rosary beads.

> One soldier was saying the rosary, his beads were around his neck and his fingers were made slippery on the beads by the blood from his neck wound, others too were busy praying. It was impossible to hear a dying man on account of the continued thunder of the big shells bursting ... I gave one poor fellow my beads; he tried to bless himself with the aid of his left arm as his right was shattered. Having moved towards another number of wounded, a shell dropped amongst them ... a shoe with a bit of leg in it and a few bits of clothing and a big hole in the ground is all that was left.

On 9 March, the Commander of the First Army, Sir Douglas Haig, enthusiastically wrote in a special order:

> We are about to engage the enemy in very favourable condition ... Reinforcements have made us stronger than the enemy in our front ... Quickness of movement is therefore of first importance to enable us to forestall the enemy and thereby gain success without severe loss.

Haig was referring to the battle for Aubers Ridge. Scheduled to start on 10 March, the aim of the British offensive was to break the deadlock of static warfare which had set in since November 1914. By taking Aubers Ridge, Sir

John French hoped that German-held Lille would be threatened.

To reach Aubers, the village of Neuve Chapelle, which in the early months of the war changed hands several times before being secured by the Germans in November 1914, had first to be retaken. The BEF now successfully broke the German-held line at Neuve Chapelle but, once this objective had been achieved, problems with supplies and co-ordination hampered attempts to advance towards Aubers Ridge. The army could advance no further and the offensive turned out to be tragic and costly, both in lives and ammunition. Seven months from the beginning of hostilities, the battle of Neuve Chapelle exemplified the now infamous nature of the war on the Western Front – enormous losses for small gains. As the casualties from the offensive began to arrive at the hospitals in and around Rouen, Sister Peterkin recorded in her diary the increased activity at the Base Hospitals.

> March 15th: There seems to be more fighting going on just now, as a great many wounded have been arriving in Rouen during the last few days. At about 2:30 this morning we saw a regular procession of ambulance cars and trains going past, up to the hospitals at the pine woods.

> March 19th: Two or three nights ago, a convoy of 60 stretcher cases arrived about 8 p.m. Most of the day sisters stayed on duty, some stayed until long after midnight ... Matron and the theatre sisters remained in the theatre hut till the small hours of the morning, lying down with blankets over them ... The camp is full up and very busy, for there are some extremely bad cases amongst them ... Some of them have the most terrible wounds, poor wretches. They say it is perfectly awful at the front just now. Some of them also say that things are not quite as good as the papers would have us believe.

The battle for Neuve Chapelle lasted from 10 to 12 March but the dates recorded in Sister Peterkin's diary show that it was three days before the injured arrived at the Base Hospitals. On 23 March, thirteen days after the battle, she made a further diary entry. 'Went to Sister Rudman's line [tent ward] today, as extra, as they are very busy there, having had a great many wounded in the other day, some very bad cases, mostly from Neuve Chapelle.' It appears inconceivable that, nearly two weeks after the battle, 'some very bad cases' were still arriving at the Base Hospitals. What was happening within the casualty handling and evacuation system?

Following the Neuve Chapelle offensive, *Punch* was selective in the information given to its readers:

> We have now six times as many men in the field as formed the original Expeditionary Force, and in the few days fighting round Neuve Chapelle

almost as much ammunition was expended by our guns as in the whole of the two and three-quarter years of the Boer War.

While the magazine was keen to illustrate the enormity of ordnance used in the battle, it failed to inform its readership that the total ground gained by the BEF was 1,200 yards on a 4,000 yard front. In the process, the BEF sustained 12,826 casualties of whom 550 officers and 12,276 were from other ranks. The deadlock of static warfare was not broken at Neuve Chapelle and the prosecution of the war became a source of concern and derision amongst some politicians and commanders. Songs and ditties composed by the men amply reflected their growing frustration and scepticism.

> I don't want to join the bloody Army,
> I don't want to go unto the War,
> I want no more to roam,
> I'd rather stay at home
> Living on the earnings of a whore.

By April 1915, the war on the Western Front had moved into a more sinister and deadly phase. Around 5 p.m. on Thursday, 22 April the Germans mounted a chlorine gas attack against the expeditionary force at Langemarck in the Ypres Salient. The use of poisonous gas had been outlawed at the 1899 Hague Conference when, on 29 July, the 'Declaration on the Use of Projectiles the Object of Which is the Diffusion of Asphyxiating or Deleterious Gases' was signed. Germany was a signatory to the Declaration but demonstrated a wilful disregard for it when a loophole was found in the agreement by which lethal gas could be dispersed.

The Germans, however, were not the first to use chemicals in The Great War. In the first month of the war, the French fired tear-gas xylyl bromide grenades against the Germans. By October 1914, the Germans, in their attempt to capture Neuve Chapelle, fired shells at the French containing a chemical designed to irritate the nasal passages and induce violent fits of sneezing. By January 1915, the Germans unsuccessfully deployed tear-gas on the Eastern Front; two months later they were using a more enhanced version of lachrymal gas against the French.

The inventor of chlorine gas, Fritz Haber, who gained a doctorate in organic chemistry in 1891, supervised its initial deployment at Langemarck in 1915. The gas was designed to asphyxiate the enemy but not before it produced severe irritation of the eyes, nose and throat. As it settled in the lungs it produced a lethal build-up of fluid, and caused corrosion of the tissues. Eventually this would lead to men coughing up and vomiting blood. In the final throws of their agonising death, men felt severe constriction of their chest, followed by frantic struggles for breath. It was a harrowing, frightening and traumatic way to die.

At the time of this first gas attack, Anthony Hossack was a rifleman, serving with Queen Victoria's Rifles. According to him, the men in his battalion had just come out of the line after a successful but gruelling attempt to take Hill 60, which had been lost by the French to the Germans in December 1914. Exhausted after three days of combat, he and his comrades were 'utterly spent and weary'.

As the men settled down to a well-earned rest and looked forward to food and sleep, their peace was shattered by 'the noise of heavy shell fire coming from the north-west, which increased every minute in volume'. Hossack noted:

> More curious than anything was a cloud of yellow grey smoke or vapour. Suddenly down the road from the Yser Canal came a galloping team of horses, their riders goading on their mounts in a frenzied way; then another and another, till the road became a seething mass with a huge pall of dust over all.

Hossack claims that officers and men stood 'dumbfounded' at what they were observing; no one knew what had happened. Then a northerly breeze brought with it

> ... a pungent nauseating smell that tickled the throat and made our eyes smart ... over the fields streamed mobs of infantry, the dusky warriors of French Africa; away went the rifles and equipment, even their tunics that they might run faster. One man came stumbling through our lines. An officer of ours held him up with levelled revolver. 'What's the matter, you bloody lot of cowards?' The Zouave was frothing at the mouth, his eyes started from their sockets, and he fell writhing at the officer's feet.

The scenes of confusion and terror amongst soldiers and civilians were witnessed by Dr John McCrae who was serving as a medical officer attached to the 1st Brigade, Canadian Artillery.

> As we moved up last evening, there was heavy firing about 4:30 on our left, the hour at which the general attack with gas was made when the French line broke ... As we sat on the road we began to see the French stragglers, men without arms, wounded men, teams, wagons, civilians, refugees ... They streamed on, and shouted to us scraps of not too inspiring information.

The 1st Canadian Division had arrived in France in February and it was to their eternal credit that, in the midst of this new weapon of warfare, they stood steadfast and carried out counterattacks with the utmost bravery. Three Canadian soldiers won the Victoria Cross for bravery and valour between 23 and 25 April.

Two days after the first attack, nurses working near the front were caught up in the gassing. Nurse Lewis of the First Aid Nursing Yeomanry Corps remembered the horror she encountered:

> Out of the queer green haze that hung over everything came an unending stream of Tommies, stumbling, staggering, gasping, and all a livid green colour. We dashed to the kitchen and prepared large quantities of salt water to help them vomit the poison.

The nurses improvised respirators with cotton wool and weak carbolic solution for the soldiers, but despite their efforts they succumbed to gas poisoning and were 'evacuated to a hospital for treatment.' There was, sadly, no treatment available for gas victims.

The use of chlorine gas took the Army, Medical and Nursing Services by complete surprise, despite the military having anticipated, several months earlier, a chemical deployment against its troops. The British had, allegedly, considered chemical warfare. According to Haig's recollection of a conversation in March 1915, Lord Dundonald had 'hopes of being able to apply an invention of his grandfather for driving a garrison out of a fort by using sulphur fumes'.

British doctors tending gas victims observed that the presence of violent coughing spasms and irritation of the eyes and the fact that 'men's buttons turn green and their bayonets black', meant that chlorine gas had definitely been used at Ypres. They concluded that 'the remedy would seem to lie in the use of respirators.'

The Director General of the Medical Services, Sir Arthur Sloggett, advised that as an antidote in the event of further gas attacks, men were to dip their handkerchiefs or whatever cloth they had available into buckets of sodium bicarbonate and then cover their mouths and noses. If no buckets of the fluid were available, which in the trenches was generally the case, it was suggested that soldiers should urinate onto a rag or pad and place it against their faces to give some relief to the effects of gas. According to the *British Journal of Nursing,* following further gas attacks on the British and Dominion Forces between April and May, 'All the men had respirators but not all were effective as the survivors explained in strained and broken voices in the hospital next day.' In a letter to the *British Medical Journal*, Major Walter Broadbent of the RAMC, who was caring for the gas casualties sent back to Britain, explained that, on examination, the men appeared to have fluid in their lungs and they found it difficult to breathe. Apparently, the men did not like oxygen therapy but preferred the tincture of benzoin placed in a steam kettle to give them some relief with their laboured breathing. According to Dr Broadbent, 'The thing which did far and away the most good was a big linseed poultice over the whole back. The men constantly asked for the poultice to be repeated.' The doctor observed that after a few days, the men had a very low urinary output, their legs became swollen and their faces very puffy. What Dr Broadbent was observing in his patients was kidney failure, which he sadly concluded was 'one of the deadly sequelae of this gas poisoning'.

Following a post-mortem carried out by Lieutenant Dr J. W. McNee, assistant to the Professor of Pathology in the University of Glasgow, it was shown that death was due to slow asphyxia caused by irritant gas. By May, there was a second wave of gas attacks. An infantry officer posted on the allied line between Boesinghe and Zonnebeke described the psychological affects of gassing.

> I fear it will be impossible for me to give you a real idea of the terror, of the awful horror, that this loathsome, noiseless wall of filthiness spread among us. I have seen men afraid, I have seen brave men nervous and apprehensive, I have never before seen brave men become suddenly panic-stricken, look round like frightened animals, forget their manhood, and their duty, and run away. Thank God! Those that did so only went a short distance before remembering they were soldiers and returned to their places.

Commenting on continuing use of gas by the Germans, the *British Journal of Nursing* stated that to nurses:

> The care of these cases has been one of their most harrowing duties during the present war, as the agony of the sufferers is so intense. The news of any treatment which affords real relief is most welcome.

Hertha Ayrton (née Sarah Marks) could not cure gas poisoning, but as an experimental physicist who specialised in vortices in water and air, she could reduce its effects. She invented a fan that could clear away noxious gases, replacing them with currents of fresh air. The system she claimed could effectively be used in the trenches. Hertha Ayrton offered, without payment, her knowledge, services and inventions to the War Office, only to be turned down by them. She later commented: 'I suppose, if I had invented something to destroy life instead of saving it, it would get taken up at once as a military proposition.' Perhaps she was right. Fritz Haber, who developed chlorine gas as a weapon of war, was awarded the 1918 Nobel Prize in Chemistry. By the summer of 1915, the Germans had introduced flame-throwers and trench mortars. Such were the effects that a British officer, commenting on the development of weapons, said that modern warfare was 'a dirty scientific business ... I'd kill all chemists and explosive experts.'

During 1915 the new weapons of death and destruction now being deployed on the Western Front had psychological as well as physical consequences for the fighting ability and morale of the troops. The strain of war was beginning to manifest itself in the number of psychological breakdown cases being referred for treatment.

Many factors ultimately destroyed the ability of men to endure the war: the enormity of losses within their battalions; the witnessing of severe wounding and mutilation amongst their colleagues; the bloated bodies of men, mules, horses and dogs that lay for days and weeks unburied; the wounded who could not be rescued; the violence of hand-to-hand combat; the separation from home and loved ones; and the daily privations of living on the Western Front. A survivor of the gas attacks in the early months of 1915 wrote:

> Till now my nerves have stood me well; but as I recall the fearful sights
> I have witnessed, and realise the majority of my pals are gone, I give way
> and break down, sobbing like a child on its mother's knee.

Psychological breakdown, or shell-shock as it was initially diagnosed, was causing controversy within the medical and military establishments. At first it was treated sympathetically, but as the numbers rose there were concerns that it was becoming a form of 'contagious hysteria' or that men were feigning their breakdowns. In the House of Lords, Earl Lytton wanted more information on the cause of war-acquired nervous breakdown and the treatments, if any, which were being made available to the men. In response, Lord Newton said that 'uncertifiables' were treated in the neurological wards of military hospitals of which there were 23 throughout the country. Defining the categories of neurological cases as being 'cases of nerve injuries caused by wounds, cases of men who were insane, cases of a minor character and cases of epilepsy', he claimed there were special treatments for each category of affliction and the War Office had 'no intention whatever of treating these unfortunate men as ordinary lunatics'. The military, however, were beginning to have a very different view; they perceived men who broke down under the strain of war to be 'lacking moral fibre' and considered shell-shock to be a predominantly 'working class' condition.

At the same time, according to the *British Journal of Nursing*: 'The cases of nervous breakdown amongst nurses on active service abroad are remarkably few.' This was an exaggeration as nurses were succumbing to depression and psychological breakdown. It was not, however, good for the image of professional nurses to appear to be breaking down under the strain of warfare. There were those who, from the safety and comfort of their own homes, reminded professional nurses that State Registration had still to be granted. It would be unhelpful to the cause if nurses did not at all times remain professional, particularly under taxing circumstances where they should remain unflappable. There were others who suggested that, once the war was over, the franchise issue should not be compromised by stories of women not being tough enough to handle the stresses and strains of war. The *British Journal of Nursing* suggested that psychological breakdown could be avoided as 'The more they [nurses] have to do the happier they are.'

Under the auspices of Lady Gifford, a Nurses' Home of Rest and Convalescence was established at Hardelot near Boulogne. The *British Journal of Nursing* acknowledges that a debt of gratitude was owed to Lady Gifford for the 'charming hospitality' being provided for nurses, where 'there is but one rule – breakfast in bed'. The perception of nurses' stamina and the attitude towards their health and care arose out of an oversimplification of complex facts. By Spring 1915 the professional nurses who accompanied the BEF to France in August 1914 were very tired. Many of them had succumbed to disease and injury. The 'Sick Sisters Tent' regularly had nurses recovering from infected fingers and hands, swollen feet and ankles, recurrent coughs and colds, gastric upsets and general debility. As nurses were permanently on their feet, many had crippling diseases of the feet and ankles; some could no longer stand or walk. Over the winter months, untreated chilblains rendered some permanently unfit for active service. One sister had a stroke and had to be sent back to Britain. Some nurses suffered from shellshock or psychological breakdown, known in the officer classes as Neurasthenia; a twenty-eight year old staff nurse who died on active service in France had 'Neurasthenia' recorded as her cause of death.

By the summer of 1915 relief was at hand for the army nurses and the number of serving QAIMNS nurses rose significantly. The work of the British Army nurses was supported by the Australian Army Nursing Service, Canadian Army Nursing Corps, New Zealand Army Nursing Service, South African Military Nursing Service, Nyasaland Nursing Service and the Queen Alexandra's Royal Naval Nursing Service. Also working on the Western Front were professional and volunteer nurses attached to the Belgian Red Cross, the French Red Cross (Croix-Rouge), the British and Irish Red Cross establishments, First Aid Nursing Yeomanry (FANY), French Flag Nursing Corps, the Scottish Women's Hospital, the Women's Sick and Wounded Convoy Corps, and Red Cross nurses from Norway, Japan, and America. A number of privately funded initiatives were established, such as the Duchess of Sutherland's and the Duchess of Westminster's ambulances and hospitals.

Sadly, the British Women's Hospital in Antwerp, established by Lady Muir Mackenzie and Mabel St Clair Stobart, had to be abandoned due to German occupation, along with two other British controlled hospitals, The English Colony Hospital managed by Nurse Edith Ward, and the British Field Hospital. The Little Allies Ambulance Corps organised by Miss Jessie Borthwick and Lady Suffolk, Lord Methuen and Sir Robert Anderson continued their work, as did Dr Hector Munro's Flying Ambulance Column. Munro brought together 25 volunteer doctors and nurses to work predominantly in Belgium. The British Brewers' Association raised money to purchase much needed ambulances and equip rest stations, as did some of the whisky companies.

Despite these initiatives trained nursing support did not grow in relation to the demand. The nursing shortage gave Ethel Bedford Fenwick the opportunity to blame consecutive governments for their handling of the Nurses Registration Bill.

> Had the expert opinion of nurses themselves, expressed over and over again for the last quarter of a century, been heeded by the Government, the shortage would never have assumed the present serious dimensions … They have pleaded for the passing of the Nurses Registration Act … Such a register would at the present moment be invaluable, both as evidence of the qualifications of nurses seeking appointments, and as affording a means of communication with trained nurses throughout the United Kingdom.

Hindsight was unhelpful – effective planning for the treatment, evacuation and distribution of casualties was really what was needed most.

\*   \*   \*   \*

The war had become a test of ingenuity for the medical and nursing services and it had become quite clear that logistical considerations in caring for the sick and injured required skilled planning and execution. The casualty care arrangements as devised by the Royal Army Medical Corps were subjected to unfavourable criticisms; the reviewers likened the treatment and evacuation arrangements of the sick and injured to a processing plant. Captain J. H. Dible, a medical officer, was scathing of the Army's treatment of casualties.

> Army hospitals, as one soon finds to one's sorrow, do not exist for the purpose of curing sick men, but for that of indexing them, supplying a name to their disease, ascertaining their religion, and booting them out elsewhere, with as much celerity as possible.

The continuation of the war with rising illness and injuries demanded a much more effective casualty clearing system. If sick and injured casualties were to have any chance of survival, there needed to be a more effective way of identifying and grading the severity of illness and injury. To ensure rapid access to care, a 'triage' system was introduced. The concept of triage involved sorting and prioritising survivable conditions, then rapidly moving them on through the lines of communication to the most appropriate treatment facilities. This was hardly a new concept, but it had either been forgotten or the military had chosen to ignore it. The origins of triage lay in the French casualty clearing arrangements developed by Baron Dominique Larrey during the Napoleonic Wars. Baron Larrey was Napoleon's Surgeon-General and realised that to sustain morale and maintain the fighting capability of the army, three factors were vital for the management of battle casualties: efficient assessment, rapid evacuation and appropriate treatment. Larrey identified that to increase survival rates, casualties had to be prioritised.

Having quickly assessed and selected the casualties with the greatest chance of survival, they needed to be rapidly removed from the battlefield and promptly transported to an appropriate treatment facility. To achieve this, field ambulances were established to move the casualties with the greatest of speed to treatment hospitals directly behind the battle lines. Now, in 1915, nearly one hundred years, several campaigns, and thousands of casualties later, the Royal Army Medical Corps designed its casualty clearing system on similar lines. The Army arranged a triage system. The first stage of the casualty handling and evacuation system took place at the 'collection zone'. From this area the men were transferred to the 'evacuation zone'. The final stage of the evacuation and treatment process was carried out at the 'distribution zone'. To facilitate this process, a series of medical intervention staging posts were established – the Regimental Aid Post, the Advanced Dressing Station, Casualty Clearing Stations and Stationary or Base Hospitals.

The Regimental Aid Post (RAP) was generally situated within the support or reserve trenches at the front line, and was also established in cellars and deserted dugouts. The complement assigned to each aid post was generally twenty-nine men, consisting of Royal Army Medical Corps (RAMC) medical officers, medical orderlies and stretcher-bearers. The medical officers trained stretcher-bearers and medical orderlies in first aid and casualty handling. The Regimental Medical Officer (RMO) was the first point of medical contact for the sick and injured troops requiring treatment.

The Regimental Medical Officer held the most advanced position in the chain of casualty treatment and evacuation. Whether in the fighting line or billets, it was his role to see that the health and welfare of his men were maintained. A good medical officer would make a point of getting to know all the officers and men and, through his interaction with them, he would be aware of their physical and psychological needs. The RMO was like a father figure to his men, but not all doctors were well disposed towards their charges. In fact, some were cynical, even contemptuous, towards their troops and frequently displayed a negative attitude at sick parades. Patrick MacGill, a stretcher-bearer with the London Irish Rifles, had gained a reputation as a highly talented writer before volunteering for war service . He described the unsympathetic attitude of one medical officer when reviewing the cases of five men and their ability to return to front line duties after a spell in hospital.

'How do you feel?' the Colonel asked the first man.
'Not well at all', was the answer. 'I can't eat 'ardly nuffink.'
'That's the sort of man required up there,' the Colonel answered. 'So up you go, and the best of luck.'
'How far can you see?' the Colonel asked the next man who complained that his eyesight was bad.
'Only about fifty yards', was the answer.
'Your regiment is in trenches barely twenty-five yards from those of the enemy,' the Colonel told him. 'So up you go, and the best of luck.'
'Off you go and find the man who wounded you,' the third soldier was told.
The fourth man confessed that he had never killed a German.
'You had better double up,' said the Colonel. 'It's time you killed one.'
When it came the turn of the fifth man, the Colonel enquired, 'How many men have you killed?'
'In and about fifty' was the soldier's answer.
'Make it a hundred then,' said the Colonel, 'and up you go and the best of luck.'

Because of this doctor's attitude, the men could never provide him with a satisfactory answer. He was either the ultimate battle hardened cynic, or a cold, uncaring practitioner. Whatever he was, he made sure the men did not profit from their conditions and experiences. It was the duty of the RMO to deal with sick parades, infestations, sanitation arrangements, food preparation and water sterilisation. He also monitored the outbreak of health conditions, such as trench foot, infectious diseases, or venereal disease. Much of the RMO's work could have been regarded as falling into the categories of 'occupational health' and 'public health'. In times of combat, he rendered immediate emergency aid both in and out of the trenches.

It was not uncommon for battalion medical officers to lose their lives while working with, or trying to reach, wounded men. The monthly obituary columns of the *British Medical Journal* attested to the fact that RMOs in the front line were inevitably exposed to injury or death. The RMO rendered basic emergency medical care at the Regimental Aid Post and ensured that casualties progressed through the 'collection zone' and on to the 'evacuation zone.' If possible, casualties would make their own way to the Regimental Aid Post or they would be carried by the stretcher-bearers.

Equipped with only a basic knowledge of first aid and a stretcher, the men who volunteered for stretcher-bearing duties were either bandsmen or from the ranks. The reassuring words, and the cigarettes they shared with the casualties, expressed their own humane feelings towards those who were suffering. In the first two years of the war, there were only sixteen stretcher-bearers to a battalion of 1,000 soldiers. The availability of stretcher-bearers for casualty evacuation was constantly affected by the high number of deaths or injuries from which they were not exempt. The killing of stretcher-bearers was highlighted in a story told to Sister Luard by two of her patients.

> Two men were telling me how they caught a sniper established in a tree, with a thousand rounds of ammunition and provisions. He asked for mercy, but he didn't get it, they said. He had just shot two stretcher-bearers.

Sick or injured men were removed by stretcher, carried on the backs of stretcher-bearers and colleagues or were dragged out in blankets, depending on trench conditions and shelling. A gruesome description of an attempt to evacuate a wounded man from the trench and take him to the RAP is given by McGill.

> I placed Barty on my back and carried him down the narrow trench. Progress was difficult … in places I had to crawl on all fours with the wounded man on my back … Two stretcher-bearers followed me carrying a wounded man on a blanket, a most harrowing business. The wounded man was bumping against the floor of the trench all the time, the stretcher-bearer in the front had to walk backwards; the stretcher-bearer in the rear was constantly tripping on the folds of the blanket. A mile of trench had to be traversed before the dressing station was reached and it took the party two hours to cover that distance.

Some trenches had overhead tram rails and the wounded were removed on a specially constructed ambulance trolley suspended from it. The deconstruction of trenches by weather and ordnance eventually made this form of casualty evacuation impracticable. Depending on the severity of shelling, gassing, climatic conditions, the state of the ground and the availability of vehicles and men, casualties were moved on to Advanced Dressing Stations (ADS) by hand, wheeled stretchers, horse drawn wagons or motorised ambulances.

The Advanced Dressing Stations were in reasonable proximity to front-line fighting and were better equipped than the RAP but could still only provide limited medical care. It was there that wounds were properly dressed and fractures were splinted; if necessary, emergency surgery was carried out and anti-tetanus serum and pain relief were administered. The Advanced Dressing Stations could be anything from a convoy of motor ambulances to a reinforced concrete bunker, farmhouse or chateau. In spite of the misery and carnage of war made evident by the broken bodies and minds arriving at the these stations, some RMOs were able to illustrate the more light-hearted side of life. In a humorous diary entry, a RMO attached to the Royal Welch Fusiliers explained the difficulties of trying to carry injured men from the trenches to the Advanced Dressing Stations.

> The Ambulance bearer work has improved; hitherto it has not taken account of the surface on which stretchers have to be carried. A wounded officer, weighing sixteen stone was carried into the advanced dressing station. He told the medical officers that his men [stretcher bearers] were toppers, he would like to kiss them all because they had only dropped him four times.

In another diary entry the MO claimed that, through abandonment, the Advanced Dressing Stations had acquired a source of nourishment for his sick and injured patients. 'The Aid Post has a cow; she gives two quarts of milk a day except after a big strafe, when she may go dry for a day with shell-shock.'

Following early medical intervention at Regimental Aid Posts and Advanced Dressing Stations, trains, motor ambulances or barges removed casualties to Casualty Clearing Stations or Base Hospitals. Casualty Clearing Stations were mobile miniature hospitals and, in the early days of the war, they were generally established in buildings. By the late summer of 1915 it became standard practice to erect, in open ground, hospital tents which could then be moved forward or back. At 12,000 yards behind the lines, the Casualty Clearing Station was supposed to be beyond the range of artillery, but they were often shelled. To make casualty transportation easier, they were generally situated near the road or rail lines. Each Casualty Clearing Station had 100 staff comprising doctors, nurses, orderlies and technicians and had the capacity to deal with 1,000 patients per day. Operating theatres and wards for acute cases were sometimes housed in army Nissen huts. There were generally six surgical teams, two of which were always on duty. Patients were classified into different wards such as those suffering from gas, fractures, gangrene, burns, enteric or trench fever. There was also the moribund tent. Here at the Casualty Clearing Stations sick and injured soldiers had their first contact with nurses whose positive effect on the men's morale is described by the war correspondent Basil Clarke.

> They followed her [the sister] about with their eyes. She stood still when her work was done and spoke to the soldier in the bed nearest her. They chatted for three or four minutes and one could see the interest of the wounded man in his steadfast gaze upon her.

The sisters had their own perception of the effect they created when men first entered the Casualty Clearing Stations. One sister remarked:

> I don't think there are many new patients who don't pass a remark to the sisters expressing how glad they are to see us. They will watch you all round the ward, and some of them, if you don't happen to speak to them will speak to you. They like to keep us talking, we have all noticed. Poor fellows, they tell us sometimes it does them more good than medicine.

The Casualty Clearing Stations had to be ready to take in large numbers of casualties at very short notice after which they were accommodated or re-classified for evacuation to the 'distribution zone'. Philip Gibbs presents a horrific picture of the wounded arriving at a one in Lillers, Belgium:

> There were men with chunks of steel in their lungs and bowels vomiting great gobs of blood, men with legs and arms torn from their trunks, men without faces, and their brains throbbing through open scalps.

The medical and nursing intervention work carried out at these stations was considered vital if patients were to survive their injuries. In the early days of the war there was very little understanding of the complex wounds the new weapons of mass destruction caused the human anatomy, and very little was understood about the resulting infections and appropriate treatment. Battles were being fought over muddy land that was filthy and infectious, ridden with human effluent and decomposing corpses of men and animals. This inevitably contributed to the seriousness of wounds. As the war progressed, medical and nursing knowledge about wound management improved. Much of it, vital for reducing morbidity and mortality, was  pioneered in Casualty Clearing Stations.

There were 64 Casualty Clearing Stations on the Western Front situated on the lines of communication. They moved from location to location as the armies advanced or retired as can be seen from the records of Casualty Clearing Station No 1 (overleaf).

| Location | Dates |
|----------|-------|
| St Omer | November 1914 – December 1914 |
| Bethune | January 1915 |
| Chocques | January 1915 – April 1918 |
| Arques | April 1918 – May 1918 |
| Elnes | May 1918 – June 1918 |
| Wavrans | June 1918 – August 1918 |
| Pernes | August 1918 |
| Ligny | August 1918 – September 1918 |
| St Flochel | September 1918 |
| Boisleux au Mont | September 1918 – October 1918 |
| Escadoeuvres | October 1918 – November 1918 |
| Mons | November 1918 – July 1919 |

In Belgium and France five flotillas of six barges were used to ferry the seriously wounded to and from Casualty Clearing Stations. The barges travelled in pairs, towed by steam tugs with a sergeant of the Royal Engineers and two sappers of the Inland Water Transport Branch in charge of navigation. Each pair of barges had a RAMC doctor, sergeant and corporal, one sister, one staff nurse, three nursing orderlies, two general duty orderlies, a cook and a cook's assistant. The barge could accommodate thirty beds. They were self-contained units allowing the staff to work and live on them. A sister based on one of the barges wrote to the *British Journal of Nursing* about her experience as a barge sister.

> I am getting used to life on a barge, quite a nice change really. I am not allowed to say where I am, but we go up and down the canal bringing wounded from the front line to Base Hospitals. We only take the worst cases, head, chests, compound fractured femurs, as this mode of transit is so much easier for the patients than a train or ambulance.

Working conditions were not always ideal, as another nurse observed how 'our barge became more and more leaky until we simply paddled from bed to bed, and then had to lie up for repairs.' A sister who had worked on a barge for nearly a year, described some of her initial duties.

> Sometimes we took patients almost straight from the firing line … Our first job then was to dress the wounds, wash all patients and get them into clean pyjamas. This was necessary as the men were nearly always verminous.

If the barges were the first choice of transport for the seriously injured or sick,

**Winter 1915: men of the Royal Army Medical Corps and Army Service Corps enjoying a 'snowball' break.**

**Men of the Royal Army Medical Corps preparing for a snowball fight.**

the hospital train ranked second as the preferred method for casualty evacuation from the forward lines. The hospital trains could move approximately 1,000 sick and injured, usually taking between six and thirty six hours to get to the Casualty Clearing Stations and Base Hospitals. Sister Luard wrote anonymously to *The Nursing Times* describing what it was like to work on a French Ambulance train with all the attendant problems of living and working in a confined space with limited facilities.

An artist's impression of a Hospital Train constructed by the Caledonian Railway Company.

> Imagine a hospital as big as King's College Hospital all packed into a train and having to be self-provisioned, watered, sanitated, lit, cleaned, doctored, nursed and staffed and officered, all within its own limits. No outside person can realise the difficulties except those who try to work it. The worst discomforts are cold, want of drinking water, lack of room for a bath, difficulty getting hot water, dirt, eccentricities in meals, bad or no lights, difficulty in getting laundry done, broken nights, want of exercise in the journey up.

On one journey her train carried 368 wounded back from the front line. Many of the casualties were in a critical condition, and nursing skills were severely stretched.

> They were bleeding faster than we could cope and the agony of getting them off the stretchers on to the top bunks is a thing to forget. All night and without a break till we got to Boulogne at 4 p.m. next day, we grappled with them, and some cases were not dressed when we got there. The head cases were delirious and trying to get out of the window, and we were giving strychnine and morphia all round.

Due to the rising casualty figures, treating the wounded whilst in transit became commonplace. Some nurses found themselves working in surroundings that could best be described as primitive. The 'straw ward' at Furnes in Belgium illustrates the challenge confronting nurses. The Church in Furnes had been made into an accommodation and treatment centre for soldiers. There were no beds, sheets, pillows or basic facilities for the nurses to care properly for the sick and injured. They only had straw for the men to be nursed upon. A medical officer attached to the nursing unit described the conditions.

I went into the straw ward on my round one wild and stormy night. Inside dozens of men lay covered with blankets on beds of straw. Most of the men were asleep, while beside one knelt a nurse with a stable lantern, holding a cup to his lips. It was a picture that an artist might have come far to see.

The sick and wounded, no matter where they came from or how they were transported, eventually arrived at the 'Distribution Zone' – the Stationary Hospitals, Base Hospitals or General Hospitals. The Base Hospitals had to be able to deal with all types of sickness and injury and they carried out many interventionist procedures. Army Medical Logistics required them to be divided into Surgical and Medical divisions. All hospitals were equipped and managed on identical principles although some were designated to specialise in particular conditions or injuries, such as ophthalmic problems, skin conditions, infectious diseases, head injuries, facial wounds and neurasthenia. Stationary or General Hospitals were normally wooden or Nissen huts, galvanised iron buildings, marquees and bell tents; sometimes, particularly in the early months of the war, they were situated in hotels or casinos. Marquees were the most favoured form of hospital accommodation and they were constructed with boarded floors, electricity and stoves. In good or warm weather one side of the marquee could be removed, thus allowing the patients to have, not only fresh air, but quite often a view of the coast. The hospitals were generally equipped with two operating theatres, X-ray facilities, dispensary and laboratories. There were bathhouses, laundries, kitchens and latrines. The hospital could usually accommodate 1,000 patients but, when there was a 'big push' on, they could expand the facilities to treat 2,000.

There were over eighty military hospitals situated in and around the French and Belgian coasts. The chart overleaf lists the names, locations and length of stay of some Stationary Hospitals and Base Hospitals.

Patients arriving at Base Hospitals were either treated there before being sent away for convalescence, or they were sent on hospital ships back to Britain for treatment in special military designated hospitals. The British Red Cross had the responsibility for transporting men from Base Hospitals to Hospital Ships. As not all Base Hospitals were situated near accessible ports, casualties marked for home embarkation were transported by Hospital Train to the quayside. The interiors of Hospital Ships which had previously been passenger vessels had been revamped to deal with casualty evacuation. They were equipped as if they were land hospitals and staffed by trained doctors and nurses. Lifts were provided for moving casualties and severe cases were nursed in swing cots as they needed to be approached from both sides. Less severe cases were assigned berths arranged in tiers. The men were allowed to sit or walk about as they pleased as long as they wore their life jackets. Once

**A temporary hospital. Some of the sick and injured were nursed on straw.**

| Hospital | Location | Dates |
|---|---|---|
| No 1 British Red Cross | Le Touquet | October 1914 – July 1918 |
| No 1 General | Le Havre<br>Etretat | August 1914 – November 1914<br>December 1914 – January 1919 |
| No 1 Stationary | Le Mans<br>Rouen | September 1914 – October 1914<br>October 1914 onward |
| No 2 British Red Cross | Rouen | September 1914 – December 1918 |
| No 2 General | Le Havre | August 1914 – May 1919 |
| No 2 Stationary | Nantes<br>Outreau<br>Abbeville | September 1914 – November 1914<br>November 1914 – September 1915<br>September 1915 – January 1920 |
| No 3 British Red Cross<br>(Friends' Ambulance Hospital) | Abbeville | October 1914 – January 1916 |
| No 3 General | Rouen<br>St Nazaire<br>Le Treport<br>Rouderbirken | August 1914 – September 1914<br>September 1914 – November 1914<br>November 1914 – March 1919<br>March 1919 onward |
| No 3 Stationary | Rouen<br>Rotterdam | February 1915 – March 1919<br>April 1919 onward |

on board, the men were given a meal and donated cigarettes were distributed amongst them.

Hospital vessels were painted white with a green band running from stem to stern, and had a large red cross painted in the middle of the ship. On night journeys they were identified by a long row of red and green lights along the taffrail on both sides of the ship. It was the Hospital Ship that saw the sick and injured on their final journey from the Western Front to 'Blighty', the term used for home or the wound that allowed them to be sent there.

It was just as well that arrangements for casualty handling and evacuation had become more organised, although not necessarily more efficient, as on 25 September, the British First Army's six divisions engaged with their French allies to launch the Artois-Loos offensive. The dispatches of Philip Gibbs who covered the days leading up to the battle alternated between cynicism and despair.

> The Scottish Troops of the 15th Division were in training for the arena, practising attacks on trenches and villages, getting a fine edge of efficiency on to bayonet work and bombing and having their morale heightened by addresses from Brigadiers and Divisional Commanders on the glorious privilege which was about to be theirs of leading the assault, and on the joys as well as duty of killing Germans ... It was the first big attack of the 15th Division. They were determined to go fast and go far. Their pride of race was stronger than the strain on their nerves.

On the right of the Scots, in the first line of attack, was the 47th London Division. Gibbs claimed:

> They too had been doped for morale; their nervous tension had been tightened up by speeches addressed to their spirit and tradition ... It was to be London's day out. They were to fight for the glory of the old town.

On the first day of the battle the army managed to push through Loos and on towards the outskirts of Lens but, as with the battle of Neuve Chapelle, they were hindered over the coming days with supply and co-ordination problems and by German counter-attacks. For the British, Loos was a short-lived success. Stretcher-bearer MacGill recorded the slaughter and his feelings for those men who bore the consequences of the battlefield.

> Another soldier came crawling towards us ... His lower lip was cut clean to the chin and hanging apart ... Men and pieces of men were lying all over the place. A leg and arm, then again a leg, cut off at the hip it might be X. Fifty yards further along I found the rest of X ... Why are all soldiers not allowed to carry morphia? How much pain it would save.

How often would it give that rest and quiet which a man requires when an excited heart persists on pumping blood out through an open wound? It would be well indeed if all soldiers were taught first-aid before the sergeant-major teaches them the art of forming fours on the parade ground.

The Artois-Loos offensive cost the BEF 50,000 casualties, half of them sustained by the 15th Scottish Division. Unfortunately, a reputation was lost as well as lives. The demands of warfare saw the British break faith with the Hague Convention and make their first chemical deployment by releasing 150 tons of chlorine gas across No Man's Land. In the fight for victory, ethical and moral imperatives were being eroded.

The casualty lists published in *The Times* were becoming mind numbing. Wives, mothers, sons and daughters were searching for information on the fate of their loved ones; there was no escape for status or class. John Kipling, a Second Lieutenant in the Irish Guards and the son of Rudyard Kipling, fell at the battle of Loos. Kipling spent the rest of his life trying to find out what happened to his eighteen year old boy. He was one of many thousands classified as 'missing in action'. The September carnage reinforced what many believed – several Christmases would pass before the war ended.

In October, the Germans caused public and international revulsion by executing a nurse. Edith Cavell had been working as a Matron in Dr Depage's School of Certified Nurses in Brussels' Barkendalle Medical Institute. At the beginning of the war, the Institute became a Red Cross Hospital at which allied and German wounded were treated. The Germans accused Edith Cavell and others of helping allied soldiers to escape across the frontier. After several weeks' imprisonment, Edith Cavell was informed on the afternoon of 11 October that a guilty judgement had been confirmed and that she was to be executed at two o'clock the following morning. In spite of diplomatic representation and pleas for clemency, notices were posted the following morning in Brussels stating that, 'Le jugement rendu contre Baucq et Cavell a déjà été executé.' (Baucq's and Cavell's sentence has already been executed.) Miss Cavell was executed at the appointed time and four others sentenced by the military tribunal met their death the same night; Philip Baucq, a Brussels architect, Louis Thuillez, a school teacher from Lille, Louis Severin, a pharmacist from Brussels, and the Countess Jeanne de Belleville. The death of Edith Cavell was a second tragedy for Dr Depage in five months. His wife, Marie, had been fundraising in America for the Belgian Red Cross. When she heard her seventeen-year old son had joined the Belgian Army she decided to return home. Tragically, Madame Depage booked a ticket on the *Lusitania* which was torpedoed by a German U-boat off the coast of Ireland with the loss of 1,200 souls.

Sister Catherine Black, who was now nursing sick and wounded soldiers in The London Hospital, reflected on the death of Edith Cavell and how, many years earlier, their paths had crossed when she had gone to work in Brussels. Waiting for her on her arrival was a note from Edith Cavell stating that she (Cavell) had been:

> ... looking forward to hearing all the news from The London Hospital and inviting me to tea with her. But although we made several appointments we never succeeded in seeing one another, to my eternal regret. We were both too busy.

The death rate amongst serving nurses was rising. In the last three months of the year, 14 nurses died by drowning. Of 29 travellers lost when the transport ship, *Marquette*, was sunk by German U boats on 23 October, 10 were staff nurses. A staff nurse was one of 87 lost on 17 November when the hospital ship *Anglia* was mined in the English Channel.

On the Western Front, as the year ended, there would be no repeat of the 1914 Christmas truce with the exchange of food, tobacco, jam, alcohol, Christmas pudding, military badges, sing-songs and football. Officially, the only exchange that took place was gunfire, artillery and, the new German weapon of warfare, phosgene gas. But according to Wilfred Ewart, an officer in the Scots Guards, there was a very brief festive interlude where he was with German soldiers on Christmas Day. In his diary he summed up the year's fighting, and the irony with which 1915 ended.

> It is Christmas morning. As I gaze over the parapet on the drab landscape before me, every feature, every rise and fall of the ground, every knoll, every hideous skeleton of shattered buildings, almost every tree, has its story ... Aubers Ridge opposite, an inconsiderable, scarcely noticeable rise in the ground ... Between the irregular lines of trenches with their sandbags and untidy earth parapets is a stream ... it runs down the middle of No Man's Land which is itself a place of coarse grasses, hiding mouldering heaps of grey and khaki, the slain of Festubert, of Neuve Chapelle and late September ... And here our men meet the Germans, so for ten brief minutes – all too brief minutes – there is peace and goodwill among the trenches on Christmas Day ... But for twenty-four hours not a shot is fired on either side. A common brotherhood of suffering or is it an act of God, or just human curiosity – has united British and Bavarian in fraternity on the battlefield this grey Christmas morning?

For the Royal Welch Fusiliers, the festive period brought to the fore some familiar concerns over the food arrangements. On Christmas Day, one officer wrote:

A company nearly lost their dinner, some of their own made off with the dixies when the cooks' backs were turned; but for carelessness in neglecting cover at the corner of the field they would have got away with it. C Company's cooks had their eyes about them … There were sing songs in the billets, and some minor casualties such as black eyes among the Drums.

On the Home Front the muted Christmas Day activities at The London Hospital were reported in *The Nursing Times:*

The patients spent a quiet but very happy Christmas in wards which had been tastefully but economically decorated with holly and evergreens; there were about 100 soldiers and 100 sailors in the hospital. On Christmas Eve the nurses made a tour of the wards singing Christmas Carols … On Christmas Day a special dinner was provided for all those who were well enough. One very pretty feature of the afternoon was the little band of children from the surgical ward, who, dressed as fairies, entertained the soldiers and sailors. Singing as they went songs taught to them by the Sisters, they trouped the Military and Naval Wards, where they gave great delight to the patients. By eight o'clock all the festivities were over, and the staff felt it had been a quieter Christmas than usual, none the less it had been a very happy one for the patients.

This would be the last Christmas at The London Hospital for Sister Catherine Black. By next year she would be working in a Casualty Clearing Station in France. Her fellow countrymen, the volunteer Irishmen of Kitchener's new Divisions, were already in France. The men of the 36th (Ulster) Division arrived in October and they spent the winter months moving around the Abbeville-Amiens-Doullens sectors of the line where it was claimed 'they suffered less from the enemy than the elements.' Departing for France at Christmas, the 16th (Irish) Division, minus 49 Brigade, marched out of their barracks to the sound of the regimental pipes and drums playing 'St Patrick's Day', 'Garryowen' and 'Come back to Erin'. Thousands did not return. Around the same time the 10th (Irish) Division was recovering from the 1915 slaughter at Gallipoli.

1915 ended tragically with the loss of many lives including three nurses when HMS *Natal* was destroyed on the Cromarty Firth by an internal explosion. Harold Bryce who was serving on board HMS *Blanche* wrote:

On New Year's Eve we were moored on the Cromarty Firth. Across the other side, at Invergordon, there was the cruiser *Natal* … There was a thunderous explosion on the *Natal*. The Chief [Stoker] said, Christ her boiler's gone up. But it was her magazine. We just stood there and

**Christmas 1915: soldiers who sustained jaw and head injuries. The horrific head and facial injuries that became all too commonplace throughout the war led to pioneering developments in neuro and reconstructive surgery.**

watched her keel over. There was a terrible loss of life, over 360. Among those killed were several naval wives and nurses from the hospital ship, *Plassey*, which was close by. They had been invited to a party aboard the *Natal*. Most of the crew were below deck … They never had a chance.

This was the second time in 1915 that service personnel in Scotland were involved in a major disaster. Earlier in the year, on 22 May, at Quintinshill near Gretna Green, there had been a multiple collision between a troop train, two coal trains, a local train and an express train. The precise number of casualties was not known but it was estimated that 227 people died and 246 were injured. It was claimed that only 60 of the 500 7th Royal Scots soldiers travelling in the troop train made it to the roll-call the following morning.

Casualties at the Western Front now stood at 892,765. Within the various nursing services, 39 women had lost their lives. And yet, the war's carnage was to continue unabated. In the coming year, the 'common brotherhood of suffering' referred to by Wilfred Ewart would demonstrate that in pursuing their goal of winning the war, the armies would not only experience a brotherhood of suffering but would share the capacity to bring about unimaginable slaughter.

Chapter VI

## *'Hanging on the Old Barbed Wire'*

# Pro Patria – Right or Wrong 1916

By 1916, patriotism was taking on a whole new meaning. On the first Sunday of the New Year, various religious denominations held a special day of intercession on behalf of 'the nation and Empire in this time of war'. The day was universally observed in the synagogues of the Jewish communities on the preceding Saturday, the Jewish Sabbath. Bishop Diggle, Bishop of Carlisle, delivered a sermon entitled 'Patriotism, true and false' during which he suggested to his assembled congregation that the 'curse of the war might bring its own blessings' and that it was a grand opportunity to cultivate 'self-discipline and patriotism'.

It was a wave of patriotism that saw men from all sections of society volunteer for war service, and it was self-discipline that allowed them to sustain the consequences of volunteering. This would be the year of Pro Patria, the name echoing an ode by Horace, the Roman poet and satirist who wrote, 'Dulce et decorum est pro patria mori', which means that 'it is sweet and right to die for my country'.

At the beginning of this year of Pro Patria, the *British Journal of Nursing* continued to make petty observations instead of dealing with the realities of life for trained nurses at the front. Referring to the attire of some serving nurses it reported that 'to meet a Red Cross nurse in France wearing white silk stockings and high-heeled white shoes, shocks one's sense of propriety, just as to meet an English [British] nurse with an untidy head, a waist faintly indicated by her apron strings, and ankles thickened by wrinkled stockings offends one's sense of patriotism.' The comment was a direct jibe at VAD nurses.

Unfortunately, the animosity continued between trained and volunteer nurses and it was exacerbated by a report produced in late 1915 by Rachel Crowdy, the Principal Commandant of the Red Cross in France. Crowdy highlighted the range of Red Cross work being carried out on the Western Front and reflected on successful interventions by members of the VAD in alleviating distress, pain, hunger and discomfort amongst the troops, both before and after the 1915 battles. Miss Crowdy claimed:

VAD members at the Rest Station worked ceaselessly, feeding the men with coffee, tea, cocoa, sandwiches, bread and butter, and doing any dressings which were urgently needed. In the long periods of quiet between the rushes, the time was filled by doing laundry work for the sisters on the trains, running lending libraries, making sand-bags, swabs, etc., for the hospitals, tracing misdirected letters for the soldiers, or doing whatever work seemed most needed... Twenty-four hours after the fighting at Loos had begun, one Rest Station was in full swing, three improvised trains with 1000 men in each were standing in the station and large boilers of cocoa were arranged to give the men hot drinks. Nurses waiting on their ambulance train and doctors from the trains waiting in the station were all pressed into service, the VAD members waiting on them and helping with the dressings... Two small hospitals run by the VAD members for men from the Army Veterinary Camp have been doing good work for many months and the Red Cross Hospitals in France have VAD members in every capacity working in them.

The report was the last straw for some trained nurses. It appeared to them that the VAD were receiving some very good press in direct contrast to the negative coverage *The Times* and *The Spectator* had recently given trained nurses, claiming they were guilty of 'ungenerous and discourteous treatment' towards VAD members. Unfortunately, their reporting accurately reflected the behaviour of some trained nurses, but it dealt a blow to the whole profession's reputation. There were certainly divisions between professional and voluntary nurses but they were not as severe as the press and journals would have had the public believe. It was unrealistic to expect that, because there was a war on, everyone working or serving together would automatically feel a sense of kinship and camaraderie. War was a cut-throat business and the nursing services were not without their share of dissenters and schemers.

As Miss Crowdy was highlighting the positive contribution the VAD made to the war effort, statements appeared in the *British Journal of Nursing* which reflected the ongoing disapproval felt by some trained nurses towards volunteer nurses. One editorial claimed that:

One of the conspicuous features of the year has been the patriotism and devotion shown by the nurses of our Overseas Dominions ... While so many nurses, with excellent certificates, are available for the care of the sick and wounded, there is no excuse for employing persons with lower qualifications.

In reality, trained nurses were not available in sufficient numbers to cope with the rising number of sick and injured casualties: VAD nurses filled a void.

Not all condemned the contribution of the VADs. According to Thekla Bowser, who worked as a member of the VAD on active service in France and had been a serving Sister of the Order of St John since 1902:

> The trained sisters have learned to appreciate the work of the VAD members and freely acknowledge that they could not possibly manage without them; whilst, on the part of the members, they give respect and willing obedience to the skilled women who have spent years in acquiring their knowledge of nursing. There is wonderfully little friction, considering the enormous numbers of people who have been thrown to work together suddenly, under somewhat difficult circumstances.

There is no doubt that many professional and volunteer nurses had polarised perceptions of each other but relations generally between the two groups were not as strained as reports implied. Furthermore, in spite of the assertions of the *British Journal of Nursing*, volunteer nurses were showing no less 'patriotism and devotion' than trained nurses.

On the military front, the French were well aware of the meaning of La Patrie: in the defence of Verdun they were dying by the thousands. The French historian, Corda, described Verdun as 'the great fortress proudly confronting the river Metz, whose name had for centuries not ceased to haunt Germanic imaginations'. For the German Chief of Staff, General von Falkenhayn, Verdun did not so much haunt his imagination as excite it. He had deduced from the previous year's fighting that:

> France has almost reached breaking point … within our reach behind the French sector of the Western Front there are objectives for the retention of which the French General Staff would be compelled to throw in every man they have.

To secure Verdun, the French were indeed compelled to throw in nearly every serving soldier; of the 330 infantry regiments of the French Army, 259 would eventually fight to secure the fortress town. It was estimated that 90,000 poilus (soldiers) per week travelled up and down the Voie Sacrée (the Sacred Way) to Verdun.

The German assault on Verdun began on 21 February 1916 and the bloodletting on both sides was immediate. Between 21 and 26 February, the French losses amounted to 25,000 men. By 27 February, in a desperate attempt to break the French line, the Germans attempted to reposition their artillery near the front of the line. For the men and horses of the gun-teams the results were calamitous. It was claimed that, on one day, 7000 horses were slaughtered, 97 of them by a single shot from a French naval gun. The artist Franz Marc, employed in camouflage work, noted that 'no man who has not experienced it can have an idea of the fantastic rage and force of the German attack … the poor horses.'

Described as 'ill-equipped', the French medical and nursing arrangements could not cope with the enormity of the Verdun carnage. There were insufficient supplies of doctors, nurses, stretcher-bearers and ambulances. The equipment needed for emergency surgery was woefully inadequate, and chloroform was almost non-existent. Henri Barbusse, a French soldier, who was later to receive critical acclaim for his book, *Under Fire*, described the pitiful sight of the sick and wounded at Verdun trying to make their way to the regimental aid posts.

> The network of trenches gets narrower and narrower and the men who are making their way towards the first-aid post from all parts of the front are multiplying and gather in the deep-dug roads … The road of desolation, with its sinister ramparts, gets narrower still. You have a feeling of suffocation, a nightmare of descent into a narrowing space … we have to stop, push our way past the dead, disturbing them as we go, while being shoved by the disordered file of those who are in continual movement towards the rear; messengers, the maimed, moaners and groaners, in desperate haste, purple with fever or pale-faced and visibly racked with pain. We have been waiting for two hours in the narrow dip at the crossing of the trench … tossed around, squeezed, stifled and blinded, climbing over one another like cattle, in a stench of blood and butcher's meat.

In France, before the outbreak of war, there had been much division and debate on the role of women in warfare. The question posed was, 'How can a woman serve France in time of war?' to which the Croix-Rouge replied, ' … les hommes au combat, les femmes à l'ambulance' (men for combat, women for ambulance work). Under the Croix-Rouge, there were three societies that cared for the casualties of war – the Socièté de Sécours aux Blessés Militaires (The Society to Aid Wounded Soldiers), Association des Dames Françaises (the Association of French Ladies) and Union des Femmes de France (the Union of Women of France). Apparently, French women regarded nursing as the equivalent of military service, a perception largely grown from the 'votes for women' debate.

Opponents of the franchise argued that, since women were exempt from military service and therefore did not pay the 'blood tax' (or 'l'impôt du sang', as the French regularly referred to it), women should not have parity of rights.

At the beginning of the war, the Croix-Rouge put 16,125 beds and 4,000 dames infirmières (nurses) at the Government's disposal for military use. In peacetime, the training of French nurses was conducted under the auspices of the Croix-Rouge. The initial course lasted four months, ending with oral and written examinations, and success led to the award of a basic diploma in nursing. Two more years of study achieved a 'superior' diploma and this extended training involved spending every morning for four months at a military or civilian hospital. France had a large number of partially trained nurses but there was a dearth of women who had undergone full training. According to the Croix-Rouge, at the time of the battle for Verdun there were only 63,000 nurses with various qualifications staffing 1,480 hospitals, dressing stations and mobile surgical units. Consequently, French medical arrangements were in danger of complete breakdown several times during the battle. Due to the huge number of French casualties and the need for fully trained nurses, many British and Irish nurses volunteered to join the Croix-Rouge or the French Flag Nursing Corps.

Ethel Bedford Fenwick, who worked for the British Committee of the Croix-Rouge, was appointed honorary superintendent and treasurer of the French Flag Nursing Corps in 1915. With her help and encouragement, 250 trained nurses went to France to support the French nursing services and by 1916, the *British Medical Journal* suggested that 3,000 British and Irish nurses were working in French hospitals. The Paris correspondent of *The Times* wrote of:

> ... some British nurses of whom we have heard very little, although that little is of great account. They are the nurses on the front, the French Front, who are working in French military hospitals under direct orders of the French military authorities and who are paid by the French Government ... They have been in bombardments, they have fought with disease, they have tactfully made their methods of nursing acceptable to the French doctors, and they have shown the mettle of which they are made by their resourcefulness in very difficult circumstances ... They are paid at the rate of £40 a year and they pay all incidental expense themselves. If they fall ill they are sent home and that is all that is done for them.

To qualify for a post in a French hospital the applicant had to be a trained nurse and had to supply the French authorities with details of nursing training: dates, medical and surgical experience, appointments held, and an employment record over a five year period. In addition to the professional requirements, she had to state how long she was prepared to serve and if she was bilingual. Two character references were required, one from a matron, and the name and address of a male next-of-kin had to be supplied. Given the shortage of trained nurses and the urgent need for them, it was curious that the French Government placed such stringent demands on fully trained British and Irish nurses. Yet, for nurses to be bi-lingual was certainly desirable; one British sister rightly illustrated the language problems that could arise with nursing care.

> The great difficulty one has, if not a fluent French speaker, is receiving orders from the doctor, as they have no time or patience to keep trying to explain again and again. When a soldier is very ill he cannot be bothered to tell of his wants to someone who does not understand, and you just have to do what you think best, but it is not always to his satisfaction, though a soldier is a most grateful man for any little attention.

A nurse, who had managed to fulfil all the requirements of the French Government and who had worked at the 'Urgent Cases' hospital at Bar-Le-Duc wrote about her experiences of nursing the wounded from Verdun.

> They arrive direct from the various dressing stations, and occasionally straight from the trenches, in a state of utter weariness, dirt and exhaustion. They are carefully removed, always under the inspection of a surgeon, to the Receiving Tent, provided and equipped for the purpose, where all their torn and soiled clothes are taken or cut off, the patients rolled into blankets and carried into the wards. These poor weary soldiers then have a blanket wash [washed in bed], are rolled into a clean bed, supplied with as much desired drink, and their wounds dressed, after which they almost invariably fall into a heavy sleep ...
>
> It is remarkable what a large part this first treatment and uninterrupted sleep plays towards their recovery in spite of their often very serious and always multiple shrapnel wounds, bullet wounds, compound fractures, burns, etc., for in quite a few days they come again, cheerful, deeply grateful, and always ready to lend a hand to their less fortunate comrades. This is my first experience of the wounded French soldier, and I find him quite delightful, always supremely plucky, except in particular cases of nervous exhaustion. He is patient, courteous, and grateful, never forgetting after his departure to send a message of thanks to those who have had him under their care ... The work is arduous, but one feels repaid on seeing large batches of these men, who arrived such pathetic wrecks of humanity, shattered and broken in mind and body, departing, shouting au revoir to their comrades, smiling, happy and full of gratitude.

In somewhat idealised dispatch, the nurse did not add that 'departing' more often than not meant going back to face the prospect of death at the front line.

Verdun made enormous demands on the French Army and there was little or no room for sentiment. The French triage system rejected medical interventions on 'hopeless cases' and the sick and wounded lived in fear that they would be labelled by the selection process as 'untransportable'. Men surviving debilitating and disfiguring wounds were of no further use as combatants and were given limited medical care. Casualties classed as survivable and functional were given the best of available care and, so that they could 'return to duty', the soldiers were medically rehabilitated for 'combat effectiveness'. The French referred to their triage philosophy as 'conservation of effectives'. The French were not alone in re-cycling their sick and wounded. A surgeon working at a British casualty clearing station lamented on the selection process for emergency treatment:

> Among so many cases, it was a sickening thing to have to make a choice for operation. We were dealing with a mass, not individuals, and, if selection had to be made, it must be in favour of those who by operation had a chance of being made fit again to return to the Front sooner or later, to keep up our man power and afford fresh fodder for the guns.

Reflecting on the slaughter at Verdun, *Punch* observed that,

> Verdun still holds out: that is the best news of the month. The French, with inexorable logic, continue to exact the highest price for the smallest gain of ground. If the Germans are ready to give 100,000 men for a hill or part of a hill they may have it. If they will give a million men they may perhaps have Verdun itself. But so far the Pyrrhic victories have stopped short of this limit, and Verdun, like Ypres, battered, ruined and evacuated by civilians, remains a symbol of Allied tenacity and the will to resist.

In France and Belgium, British and Irish nurses were showing more than tenacity and a will to resist when, in addition to working in Casualty Clearing Stations and hospitals, they went to work in the trenches. The work was little more than first-aid but it was designed to militate against the onset of shock from blood loss. One of the first women to identify the problems of untreated shock was Elsie Knocker, a trained nurse from England and a member of Dr Hector Monro's Women's Emergency Corps. It occurred to her that 'a great many of the dead men brought in by the ambulances had not been seriously wounded and that the men had died mostly from shock.' Consequently, she approached the Belgian military authorities and requested permission, as a trained nurse, to go and live in and around the trenches, and treat the men directly they were injured. She was assisted in this venture by Mairi Chisholm, an eighteen-year old Scottish volunteer nurse. Elsie Knocker claimed that the military gave them 'twenty-four hours to stand the strain of life in the trenches, and even that would be too much'. But eighteen months on from her initial proposal, she and Mairi Chisholm were still working close behind the trenches and running an emergency casualty treatment station at Pervyse. For the two women, trench life was no better than for the men when it came to sleeping, washing and dressing. According to Elsie Knocker:

> We slept in our clothes and cut our hair short so that it would tuck inside our caps. Dressing meant simply putting on our boots. There were times when we had to scrape the lice off with the blunt edge of a knife and our underclothes stuck to us.

It was highly unusual for women to work near the trenches and John Redmond MP who visited the women at their aid post claimed that 'it is not surprising that the Belgian people look upon them with a sort of supernatural and sacred love.' For their work in caring for Belgian soldiers, King Albert of Belgium awarded both women the Order of Leopold II. Miss Chisholm was the youngest person to receive the honour.

Working for the Croix-Rouge: nurses leaving a trench. It was estimated that as many as 3,000 British and Irish Nurses worked with the Croix-Rouge. Trench work, however, was uncommon.

While British and Irish nurses were working under the thunder of guns in France and Flanders, their colleagues in Ireland were about to deal with the casualties of a planned insurrection in Dublin.

Working class Dubliners were living in the worst slums in the United Kingdom and North West Europe. A 1914 Government report had highlighted the fact that 'thirty-seven per cent of the entire working-class of Dublin lived in a density of more than six persons to a room: fourteen per cent declared unfit for human habitation.' So bad were the living conditions, it was claimed that 'the trenches are safer than the Dublin slums.' In the year preceding the war, the Irish Transport Union decided to take on the owner of the Dublin Tramways, the ill-advised confrontation resulting in a long and, at times, brutal industrial struggle. The result for the trade unions was defeat and many lost their jobs or were refused reinstatement. In what was already a seriously socio-economically depressed city, the effect of the strikes only added to the feelings of social impotence among the working classes. The south of Ireland had no strong industrial base. Most Dubliners were employed in service industries while many were unemployed. It required little imagination to realise that the working classes with dire economic and social circumstances were ripe for recruitment propaganda and the city of Dublin became fertile ground for the army recruiting officers. Tragically, men could earn more by offering their lives than in the low-wage jobs at home. In addition to the increased wages offered by enlistment, further remuneration for families was available in the form of 'separation' and 'dependant' allowances. For many British and Irish families living in abject poverty, the war offered some economic respite.

Apart from the prospect of deliverance from economic hardship, the propaganda campaigns were designed to appeal to Christian principles and beliefs and to a sense of patriotism, honour, masculinity, sacrifice, duty and obligation. One particular poster entitled 'What have you done for Ireland?' focused on evoking feelings of guilt and patriotism.

What Have You Done For Ireland?
How have you answered the call?
Are you pleased with the part you are playing
In the job that demands us all?
Have you changed the tweed for the khaki
To serve with the rank and the file
As your comrades are gladly serving,
Or isn't it worth your while?
Can you meet the eyes of the soldiers?
Or have you to turn away?
When they talk of the stay-at-home slacker,
Have you never a word to say?
When you read the Roll of Honour
Of living and dead what then?
Does the voice within approve you
As one to be ranked with men?
For if in Ireland's glory
Each soldier may claim his share,
So he who would shirk his duty,
His burden of shame must bear.
You who are strong and active,
You who are fit for the fray,
What have you done for Ireland?

Believing that it was their patriotic duty, many Irishmen filled the ranks of the British Army. However, this gesture was no guarantee that, in their absence, others would not exploit the war situation. In April 1916, while the men of the 16th (Irish) Division were engaged in heavy fighting on the Hulluch sector of the Loos Salient, their fellow countrymen and women staged a rebellion in Dublin. On Easter Monday, in full public view, an alliance of around 150 men from the Irish Republican Brotherhood, the Irish Volunteers and the Irish Citizen Army assembled at Liberty Hall where, without interruption, they proceeded to march to the General Post Office. They were part of a 1,000 strong band of insurgents and, after commandeering the GPO which had been chosen as their Headquarters, they hoisted a tricolour and a green banner with the words 'Irish Republic' inscribed on it. Patrick Pearse, a headmaster and self-styled defender of Irish freedom, stood at the front of the GPO and read a Proclamation.

IRISHMEN AND IRISHWOMEN:
In the name of God and of the dead generations from which she receives her old tradition of nationhood, Ireland, through us, summons her children to her flag and strikes for her freedom. Having organised and trained her manhood through her secret revolutionary organisation, the Irish Republican Brotherhood, and through her open military organisations, the Irish Volunteers and the Irish Citizen Army, having patiently perfected her discipline, having resolutely waited for the right moment to reveal itself, she now seizes that moment, and, supported by her exiled children in America and by gallant allies in Europe, but relying in the first on her own strength, she strikes in full confidence of victory.

We declare the right of the people of Ireland to the ownership of Ireland, and to the unfettered control of Irish destinies, to be sovereign and indefeasible. The long usurpation of that right by a foreign people and government has not extinguished the right, nor can it ever be extinguished except by the destruction of the Irish people. In every generation the Irish people have asserted their right to national freedom and sovereignty; six times during the past three hundred years they have asserted it in arms. Standing on that fundamental right and again asserting it in arms in the face of the world, we hereby proclaim the Irish Republic as a Sovereign Independent State and we pledge our lives and the lives of our comrades-in-arms, to the cause of its freedom, of its welfare, and of its exaltation among the nations ...

So the Easter Rising began. In their attempt to establish a 'Sovereign Independent State', the insurgents took over public and commercial buildings which they believed had significant strategic importance. It was in and around those buildings that heavy fighting took place and parts of the city of Dublin and some of the suburbs came to resemble the ruined buildings of the Western Front. Between Monday 24 and Sunday 30 April, at least 1,300 military personnel, civilians and insurgents were killed, wounded or went missing.

*The Nursing Times* announced that the 'sudden and insane rising in Ireland, with its almost incredible scenes in the streets of Dublin, came as a shock to us all.' Dispatches sent from Irish nurses to the journal claimed that on Easter Monday 'Sir Patrick Dun's Hospital was filled to overflowing with the wounded from the Mount Street fighting, and The National Maternity Hospital opened its doors for the treatment of casualties.' According to the reports, members of Sir Patrick Dun's nursing staff 'at considerable risk to themselves, under machine-gun and rifle fire, managed to secure much needed supplies for the hospital.' A midwife, Mrs Catherine Nelson, along with Miss Louisa Nolan, were the first to render emergency assistance to the wounded soldiers fighting at Mount Street Bridge. Miss Nolan's work and bravery were considered:

> ... exceptional as she dashed out of a house and ran like a deer right in the face of the hail of sniper bullets. She grasped a wounded soldier under the arms, and dragged him to where others were ready to carry him to hospital. Then back she ran for another stricken man.

For her bravery during the 'Irish Rebellion', Miss Louisa Nolan was awarded the Military Medal, along with Miss Florence Ada Williams. Further reports stated that nurses from Sir Patrick Dun's Hospital 'advanced with their hands raised, one of the nurses waving a towel as a white flag, going to the succour of a number of soldiers lying near the Bridge.' Eye-witness accounts claimed that nurses 'attended to the wounded as they fell, carried them out of the firing line, and conveyed them safely past the rebel strongholds to the hospital.'

On Easter Monday, the medical and nursing staff of the Richmond Hospital were reported to be working under 'considerable strain'. The first casualty to arrive at the hospital was a two-year old boy who had been shot through the head. He had been brought to the hospital by Father Albert, a priest from Church Street. Reverend Father Aloysius reported that:

> Shortly after 12 o'clock we were at luncheon, we were startled by rifle fire, and very soon, word was brought to the Friary that a little boy had been shot near the Father Mathew Hall.

As the fighting intensified, there were fears that patients could be vulnerable to sniper fire from the surrounding roof-tops so staff at the Richmond took the precaution of transferring patients from their beds to mattresses on the hospital floor. According to *The Nursing Times*, 'Very valuable service was rendered to the wounded by the staff of the Royal City of Dublin Hospital.' The Matron explained that, following the outbreak of the rebellion:

> ... practically the whole time we were under fire. Bullets came into the operating theatre, into a sister's bedroom, and into the nurses' dining room. We had to turn the dispensary into a wound-dressing room.

The Matron, nursing sisters, nuns and staff nurses at Jervis Street Hospital attended to cases, both in and out of the hospital. The first cases to arrive in the hospital on Easter Monday were four dead soldiers and a female civilian. On one occasion, an injured woman was lying in Middle Abbey Street requiring urgent medical attention. The doctors at Jervis Street were already heavily engaged when the request for help came to the hospital. Two nurses, under trying conditions, carried the woman back for treatment and care. During the week of fighting, the hospital staff dealt with between 600 and 700 cases: 43 died in the hospital, and 38 fatalities were brought in. At Mercer's Hospital, 130 people were treated for gunshot wounds, one of them being a sixteen-year old soldier.

> The Mater Misericordiae Hospital claimed it had a: heavy casualty list and Dr Steevens' Hospital attended to one hundred casualties. The Adelaide had 75 military and civilian cases, five being fatalities. St Vincent's cared for 45 casualties, some brought in dead, others dying shortly after admission. The Rotunda, according to the Lady Superintendent, had an 'extremely anxious time. Two bullets entered ward 7, causing great alarm to the patients who were then moved out to the back of the hospital. The hospital became very full; one day there were 113 patients in the wards.

At Dublin Castle Red Cross Hospital, there were already 67 soldiers recovering from wounds sustained in France when a further 118 wounded soldiers were admitted. Supported by members of the VAD, 34 wounded insurgents, 20 civilians and 2 police officers were cared for by the medical and nursing staff. Dr Ella Webb and members of the VAD hastily converted the Irish War Hospital Depot at Merrion Square into a thirty-bed hospital and three hours later it carried out its first operation. For nearly a week, the Dublin hospitals laboured under the strain of bombardments from machine gun, rifle, and sniper fire. As it was impossible for trades people to deliver goods, hospitals had to cope with diminished food and medical supplies. The staff worked on restricted diets, conserving food for their patients, and there were water, electricity and gas shortages. Doctors, nurses and auxiliary staff worked for days and nights without relief due to the military authorities' restrictions which made it impossible for many people, including hospital staff, to travel to their work.

Writing in the *British Journal of Nursing*, a nurse gave her 'eye-witness' account of the week's activities.

> I went with some nurses to help with the temporary hospital, [Irish War Hospital Depot] and for over a week we helped to nurse the gallant Sherwood Forresters, who were badly hit when arriving in Dublin. None of them liked the 'job' they were on, and one could not wonder. The ruin of the city is terrible. I went for a drive as far as the Rotunda Hospital. In Sackville Street there is desolation; it reminds one of the pictures of Ypres! The post office is a shell, and Eason, our large newspaper place, ruined. The looting in that part was very bad, women in bare feet going about in coats worth £100, black silk dresses on top of rags, diamond rings and gold watches were offered for 1 and 2 shillings (five and ten pence), and pianos were taken and quarrelled over! The tales of sorrow and ruin are distressing, and one wonders what can be the 'ideals' of this Sinn Fein Society, which will allow its members to cause such distress and suffering to their fellow countrymen.

On 29 April, Patrick Pearse declared a cease-fire. He requested a volunteer nurse, Elizabeth O'Farrell, to act as an intermediary between the insurgent leaders and the British Military authorities. She was a member of the Cumann na mBan (The Women's Organisation of Irish Volunteers) and one of 40 women attached to the insurgents' HQ at the GPO. When it became clear the insurrection was doomed and the GPO could no longer be held, Pearse instructed all the women to leave. Only Miss O'Farrell and two others, Julia Grenan and Winnie Carney, were left to attend to the wounded insurgents and administrative work. According to Miss O'Farrell: 'On Saturday 29 I went with a message from Commandant Pearse to the Commander of the British Forces.' It was believed to contain the terms of peace. She delivered a note from General Lowe to Patrick Pearse, then 'at about 3:30 that afternoon, General Lowe received Commandant Pearse at the top of Moore Street.' Miss O'Farrell accompanied Patrick Pearse to the meeting with General Lowe when Pearse surrendered.

In a bid to establish a Republic, the rebellion had exacted a high price. Sadly, in their fight for freedom, some idealistic men left behind dependants: Patrick Flannigan, killed at North King Street, left a wife and three children; Michael Mallin, executed at Kilmainham, left a wife and five children; and Patrick Doyle, killed in the fighting at Clanwilliam House, also left a wife and five children. The youngest to die in the insurrection was a two-year old boy, the eldest a 79 year-old man. Of the total number of deaths, 20 were under the age of 15. A nurse, Miss Keogh, was shot dead while on duty, and Mr W.

Maguire, killed while engaged in ambulance work, left a wife and seven children. While going to the aid of an injured soldier, Mr Holden Stodart, the Corps Superintendent for County Dublin St John's Ambulance Brigade, was shot dead, leaving a wife and child. The estimated number of wounded amongst the military, civilian, police and insurgents was between 600 and 1000. It was estimated that 300 people lost their lives; 60 of the dead were insurgents. This figure does not include the leaders and key insurgents executed by the British military authorities.

By executing the leaders of what they considered to be a rebellion, the British military authorities had inadvertently secured the memory of their 'martyrdom' in the national psyche and changed the course of Irish history. During the week of the Easter Rising in the Loos Salient, the 16th (Irish) Division sustained 1,980 casualties. Of these 232 were killed by shelling, 338 were killed by gas poisoning, 488 were wounded by exploding shells, and 922 suffered the effects of gassing. Tragically, the sacrifices made by Irishmen fighting in the British Army for the freedom of small nations, including their own, would be consigned to the social, political and historical wilderness.

By the summer of 1916, on the Western Front, Douglas Haig, the new Commander-in-Chief, was being persuaded by the French to open an offensive in the area of the Somme. In December 1915, Haig, in what can only be described as an act of ungallant behaviour, contrived successfully to have Sir John French removed from his position. French might have reflected on the last words of Edith Cavell: 'I now know that patriotism is not enough. I must have no hatred or bitterness towards anyone.' To secure his position as Commander-in-Chief, Sir John French required more than patriotic credentials. In his farewell order to the Army he wrote:

> In relinquishing the Command of the British Army in France, I wish to express to the officers, non-commissioned officers and men, with whom I have been so closely associated during the last sixteen months, my heartfelt sorrow in parting with them before the campaign, in which we have been so long engaged together, has been brought to a victorious conclusion ...

French's next four paragraphs contained emotive words such as 'conviction', 'success', 'tenacity', 'courage', 'pride', 'glory', 'magnificent qualities', 'beloved comrades' and 'greatest sacrifice'. He concluded poignantly:

> In saying good-bye to the British Army in France, I ask them once again to accept this expression of my deepest gratitude and heartfelt devotion towards them, and my earnest good wishes for the glorious future which I feel to be assured.

The disastrous 1915 campaigns with limited strategic success and rising attrition rates were partly the cause of French's downfall. Writing home, a soldier summed up the experiences of the many involved in the 1915 battles.

> I want to forget those days and nights; my hands often bloody, and I saw many a man killed, or watched him die. It seems now but a nightmare. Several comrades of mine are in 'Blighty' with shell shock and shattered nerves; war lovers should see some of these cases when they are here, and then you will see some of the horror, the awful madness, and torture of war ... Sir John French reported that in his visits to most of the field hospitals, the optimism of the wounded was remarkable. It is not. What is remarkably, wonderfully impressive is the self-control of many men under a bombardment, the grand self-restraint, the heroic self-pride that keeps you (some of you) calm and steady in the won't-give-in spirit, the won't-appear-frightened resolve that's what saves the line. The concussion is enough to kill you if you are close enough. Heavy explosive is awful stuff when it explodes; one's insides get an awful lift. After a series of such strains one jumps at the crack of a rifle, and the ping, pong of a bullet, and then bombs are as loud as shells. Yes 'tis the afterwards, too. You don't look much different, I suppose, but if you have a few months of such liveliness and we have had a fair all round experience one's nerves are far different from what they were in Angleterre. One good thing is, I have (I now know) quite strong nerves, and was able to do, as much as was possible, my duty.

Letters from the front such as this probably assisted with French's fall from grace. What the Government wanted was a man who could win the war; by appointing Douglas Haig, some believed they had found that man. Haig's remit was to secure a victory but to 'avoid heavy losses and wastage'. Ironically, this man would exact *l'impôt du sang* on the British, Irish and Dominion forces that could not possibly have been foreseen by politicians or imagined by a patriotic public. Brigadier General H. J. Evans believed the military high command wanted 'butchers not brigadiers'. Brigadier General Evans eventually fell foul of his superiors when he refused to sacrifice the lives of his men at Mametz Wood on the Somme. The Somme offensive was supposed to relieve the pressure on the French at Verdun. In reality, there were political and military agendas being played out. Joffre, the French Commander had calculated that if French casualty rates continued at the February and March levels, then, by the end of May, 'the French Army would cease to exist'. Even so, the offensive would open on 1 July 1916.

The month before the Anglo-French offensive was launched Haig forewarned that:

The nation must be taught to bear losses. No amount of skill on the part of the higher commanders, no training, however good on the part of the officers and men, no superiority of arms and ammunition, however great, will enable victories to be won without the sacrifice of men's lives. The nation must be prepared to see heavy casualty lists.

Of the French at Verdun, *Punch* recorded that 'they continue to exact the highest price for the smallest gain of ground'. Before the end of the year, this would be true of all belligerents

On 30 June, the day before the first Somme battle, Haig's diary was upbeat.

The men are in splendid spirits. Several have said that they have never before been so instructed and informed of the nature of the operation before them. The barbed wire has never been so well cut, nor the artillery preparation so thorough. All the commanders are full of confidence.

On 1 July, a British newspaper carried the headlines 'British Offensive Begins – Official.' The optimistic rather than truthful reporting went on to state:

About half-past seven o'clock this morning a vigorous offensive was launched by the British Army. The front extends over 20 miles north of the Somme. The assault was preceded by a terrific bombardment, lasting about an hour and a half. It is too late to give anything but the barest of particulars, as the fighting is developing intensity, but the British troops have already occupied the German front lines.

According to Philip Gibbs:

It was our offensive that the German Command feared most, for they had no exact knowledge of our strength or the quality of our new troops. They knew that our army had grown prodigiously since the assault on Loos.

The men who fought on the Somme were the soldiers of Kitchener's New Armies. They were the volunteers who, in the opening months of the war, enthusiastically signed up for war service. The ranks of the new armies were filled with thousands-upon-thousands of men from all classes, backgrounds, trades, occupations, the unemployed and dispossessed. They came from the cities, towns and villages of Scotland, England, Wales and Ireland, joining up in large community groups forming 'Chums' or 'Pals' battalions. In addition, there were large occupational groups of men such as dockers and miners who had enlisted together. The Earl of Derby, who did much to encourage enlistment, managed to exact a guarantee from Lord

Kitchener that those who 'joined together would serve together'. Kitchener was as good as his word and in the coming months, on the Somme, those patriotic, enthusiastic volunteers, would serve and die en masse together.

For a week before the attack on 1 July, the British artillery carried out a relentless bombardment on the German front line in the belief that their trenches and fortifications would be destroyed. One British soldier commented that by destroying the dug-outs, wire entanglements and gun emplacements, the assault would be a 'cake-walk'. According to Philip Gibbs,

> The German Command expected a heavy blow, and prepared for it… What confidence they had of being able to resist the British attack was based upon the wonderful strength of the lines which they had been digging and fortifying since the autumn of the first year of the war, 'impregnable positions' they called them.

What was expected by the British High Command, and thousands of trusting soldiers, to be a battle without effort, turned out to be one of the most heinous, traumatic and unbelievable military blunders in the history of warfare. The German trenches were almost impregnable and their fortifications following days of artillery bombardment were not destroyed.

Stefan Westmann, a German Medical Officer, summed up the German response to the British bombardment and attack of 1 July:

> Then the British went over the top. The very moment we felt their artillery fire was directed against the reserve positions, our machine-gunners crawled out of their bunkers, red-eyed and dirty, covered in the blood of their fallen comrades, and opened up a terrific fire.

Battalion after battalion was thrown into the maelstrom; the 10th West Yorkshire, 1st Newfoundland, 4th Tyneside Scottish, 1st Tyneside Irish, Donegal and Fermanagh Volunteers, 1st Hampshires, Accrington Pals, Leeds Pals, 1st King's Own Scottish Borderers, 1st Bradford Pals, 1st Edinburgh City Battalion, 1st Royal Inniskilling Fusiliers, Sheffield City Battalion and many more suffered appalling casualties on the first day. Under relentless fire, the British and Dominion Forces sustained 60,000 casualties – 20,000 dead and 40,000 wounded or missing. Racked with bullets, mutilated by shells or hanging on uncut barbed wire, enthusiasm, valour and patriotism died obscene deaths.

Preparations for the offensive had been made on a gigantic scale, and the High Command estimated that the casualties would be cared for by 19 main dressing stations, 39 of them advanced ones, and 9 posts for the walking wounded; 12 ambulance trains and 6 improvised ambulance trains were to be made available for the removal of the wounded. The Commander of the Fourth Army, Sir Henry Rawlinson, estimated that 10,000 casualties per day would require to be transported in this manner. On that tragic day, in spite of the triage and casualty evacuation system, the medical and nursing services were overwhelmed once again. In the first twenty-four hours of the battle, 26,675 wounded were collected from the battleground. As there were not enough stretcher-bearers nor transport to cope with the volume of injured men requiring care and transportation to the appropriate medical facilities, the casualty evacuation system came under intolerable pressure. Prior to the Somme offensive, it had been decided to increase the number of stretcher-bearers attached to each battalion from 16 to 32. The increase had little effect as stretcher-bearers themselves became casualties while out searching for the wounded. Men not directly involved in the fighting, such as the Labour Corps, engineers and artillerymen, were commandeered as stretcher-bearers but there were not enough stretchers. One sergeant claimed they were forced to carry two wounded men to a stretcher. Improvised stretchers were made from blankets, webbing, clothing, corrugated iron and wooden planks, jackets and poles. The Regimental Aid Posts, Field Ambulances, Dressing Stations and Casualty Clearing Stations were full. One Field Ambulance report written at 7 p.m. stated:

> Urgent demand for more stretchers, indented on CCS Corbie without avail. 8.30 p.m. 36 CCS and 38 CCS at Heilly closed. By midnight choked with cases, opened several barns for temporary accommodation.

In the town of Albert, the basilica of Notre Dame des Brèbiers was used as a dressing station. In June 1915, the church had been struck by a shell and the effigy of the Virgin and Child mounted on the steeple was bent down to a 15° angle. Amongst the troops, there was a superstition that when the effigy fell, the war would end. For the hundreds of wounded lying inside the basilica, the suspended Virgin and Child had not fallen quickly enough. One stretcher-bearer described the scene inside what was left of the church:

> Wounded flooded in on foot, or were brought by stretchers, wheelbarrows, carts anything … Soon the whole church was packed and we were ordered to stop any vehicle that passed and make them take the wounded to the rear … Those who were not expected to survive were put on one side and left. It was very hard to ignore their cries for help but we had to concentrate on those who might live.

A Frenchman attached to the staff of General Gough went to Albert on the evening of 1 July and saw that:

**One of 64 Casualty Clearing Stations established on the Western Front, where the bulk of emergency interventions and life-saving surgery was carried out.**

Ambulances were taking away the wounded from the casualty clearing station in Albert. Lorries were packed with the lighter casualties who waited their turn in big groups, all labelled with the nature of their wounds.

Eighteen ambulance trains, promised and much needed, failed to materialise. Moving the men to Casualty Clearing Stations and on to Base Hospitals therefore became an impossible task, and created even greater congestion. At 11 p.m., it was noted by the Director of Medical Service, Fourth Army, that 'Ambulance Trains not yet arriving and all CCS in Southern Area are full except for those at Vecquement and these are filling rapidly.' By midnight, only five ambulance trains had been in service, three during the day, with two additions in the evening.

How many of Kitchener's volunteers died that day for the want of stretcher-bearers, transport, surgeons, nurses, pain relief, water and warmth?

How many suffered and died alone, or struggled to set their wounded bodies free as they hung on the uncut wire? How many watched the life ebb out of the shrapnel torn bodies of their comrades before it became their turn to die obscenely?

Before the offensive began, Philip Gibbs toured the British medical facilities and was present as the casualties began to arrive.

It was with a rush that their first cases came, and the tide did not slacken … Three thousand wounded came to Daours on the Somme, three thousand to Corbie, thousands to Dernancourt, Heilly, Puchevillers, Toutencourt, and many other 'clearing stations'. At Daours the tents were filled to overflowing, until there was no more room. The wounded were laid down on the grass to wait their turn for the surgeon's knife. Some of them crawled over to haycocks and covered themselves with hay and went to sleep, as I saw them sleeping there, like dead men. Here and there shell-shocked boys sat weeping or moaning, and shaking with an ague. Most of the wounded were quiet and did not give any groan or moan.

Haig, however, was optimistic about the 'success' of the first day's operations.

Very successful attack this morning … All went like clockwork … The battle is going very well for us and already the Germans are surrendering freely. The enemy is so short of men that he is collecting them from all parts of the line. Our troops are in wonderful spirits and full of confidence.

This was not the perception of those who witnessed the human cost of the battle. On 2 July, George Coppard, a machine gunner, surveyed the scene in front of his trench and saw that:

Hundreds of dead were strung out like wreckage washed up to a high water mark. Quite as many had died on the enemy wire as on the ground … They hung there in grotesque postures. Some looked as though they were praying: they had died on their knees and the wire had prevented their fall. From the way the bodies were evenly spread out, whether on the wire or lying in front of it, it was clear that there were no gaps in the wire at the time of the attack. The Germans must have been reinforcing the wire for months.

Stunned into disbelief, Coppard could not understand why the High Command overlooked what he believed were the practicalities of planning such an ambitious offensive.

How did our planners imagine that Tommies, having survived all the other hazards and there were plenty in crossing No Man's Land would break through the German wire? Had they studied the black density of it through their powerful binoculars? What made them think that artillery fire would pound such wire to pieces? Any Tommy could have told them that shell-fire lifts wire up and drops it down, often in a worse tangle than before.

The cost of the first day's offensive was becoming all too clear. After visiting a hospital at Corbie, Philip Gibbs stated:

> I had to wipe cold sweat from my forehead, and found myself trembling in a queer way. The hospital was christened the 'Butcher's Shop' by a colonel of the RAMC. 'This is our Butcher's Shop,' he said, cheerily. 'Come and have a look at my cases. They're the worst possible; stomach wounds, compound fractures, and all that. We lop off limbs here all day long, and all night. You've no idea!' I had no idea. I did not wish to see its reality ... Yet, I argued, what men are brave enough to suffer I ought to have the courage to see ... I saw and sickened. In one long, narrow room there were about thirty beds, and in each bed lay a young British soldier or part of a young British soldier. There was not much left of one of them. Both his legs had been amputated to the thigh and both his arms to the shoulder-blades ... another case of the same kind; one leg gone and the other going, and one arm ... I spoke to that man. He was quite conscious, with bright eyes. His right leg was uncovered, and supported on a board hung from the ceiling. Its flesh was like that of a chicken badly carved – white, flabby, and in tatters. In bed after bed I saw men of ours, very young men, who had been lopped of limbs a few hours ago or a few minutes, some of them unconscious, some of them strangely and terribly conscious, with a look in their eyes as though staring at the death which sat near to them, and edged nearer ... I walked stiffly out of the 'Butcher's Shop', past the man who has lost both arms and both legs, that vital trunk, past rows of men lying under blankets, past a stench of mud and blood and anesthetics, to the fresh air of the gateway, where a column of ambulances had just arrived with a new harvest from the fields of the Somme.

It was a day of unimaginable slaughter, accompanied by individual and collective acts of supreme bravery. Nine Victoria Crosses were awarded for acts of valour. It is surprising that even more VCs were not awarded considering the sacrifices made by men attempting to take their objectives on 1 July. But, for all of the tragedy of the first day, the weeks and months ahead were to be no better as division after division was offered up to the gluttonous appetite of the guns. It was killing on an industrial scale and, in order to keep the offensive supported, thousands upon thousands of men, horses, guns and all manner of accoutrements for waging war were sent up and down the lines.

A census of military traffic passing Fricourt Cemetery between 21 and 22 July illustrated the magnitude of the Somme operation:

> 26,536 Troops, 13 Gun Carriages, 95 Buses, 813 Motor Lorries, 568 4-Horse Wagons, 63 Guns, 515 1-Horse Carts, 350 Ambulances, 568 Motor Cars, 1,458 6-Horse Wagons, 1,215 2-Horse Wagons, 5,404 Horses, 1,043 Cycles, 10 Machine Guns.

The prosecution of the war was demanding more and more of men and beasts. Yet, in spite of the discipline, loyalty and duty shown by the men, and the sacrifices they made on the opening weeks of the offensive, there were still some officers who believed in making examples of men they perceived to be 'lacking discipline'. At Dernancourt on the Somme, Max Plowman, a subaltern in the 10th Battalion, West Yorkshire Regiment, noted:

> There is a boy in D Company doing Field Punishment No 1 … his outstretched arms are tied to the wheel of a travelling field-kitchen. The regimental sergeant major has just told me that the boy is there for falling out of the march … and two men being marched up and down in the blazing heat … I do not know for what offence they are doing 'pack-drill' but it is depressing to see them, loaded with rifles and full packs, going to and fro over a piece of ground not more than twenty yards long. Volunteers going shortly into battle! I think with almost physical sickness of the legends that sustain our arm-chair patriots at home.

From July to December, 66 men were executed for allegedly casting away arms, cowardice, desertion, murder, mutiny, quitting their posts, and striking a senior officer. Prior to the Somme offensive, between January and June, forty executions had been carried out.

What was going on in the minds of those men and just how vulnerable, fragile and susceptible had they become? A medical officer, Charles McMoran Wilson, later to become Lord Moran, noticed a visible change in his men after their experience of battle.

> All around me are faces which sleep might not have visited for a week, and they have dark shadows under eyes that are older, more serious. Some that were lined before look ill, and boys have lost their freshness in a month. Voices too are tired and the very gait of men has lost its spring. The sap has gone out of them, they are dried up.

Charles McMoran was able to evidence the physical changes in the men, but it was not so easy to detect what was happening to their minds. The battles on the Somme were exacting many psychological casualties, but some medical officers still regarded traumatised men as having 'no more than a dose of funk.' An officer from the 4th Battalion, Oxford and Buckinghamshire Light Infantry, was distressed by an incident involving a soldier who had been on the Western Front since 1914.

> We were out at rest behind the line during the battle of the Somme. I was told one morning that a private in my company, who had been out since the beginning of the war, was unfit to go on parade. But the doctor had passed him fit … When I went to see him I came to the conclusion that he was in a very serious mental condition. I told him he was not to go on parade and I reported the matter to the commanding officer. He told me it was not for me to decide, only the medical officer, and that he should be made to get up and go on parade. Later in the morning this chap shot himself.

Shell-shock, or neurasthenia, as it was referred to among officers, could be an insidious condition. According to Frank Richards of the Royal Welch Fusiliers, after their attempt to capture High Wood:

> One of our old stretcher-bearers went mad and started to undress himself. He was uttering horrible screams, and we had to fight with him and overpower him before he could be got to the Aid Post. He had been going queer for the last month or two.

A medical officer who observed the repressed psychological manifestations of warfare in some of his men when they returned to billets after their involvement in the battle for Mametz Woods stated:

> Some, even of the hard bitten, showed signs of the strain through which they had passed now there was no more need to key themselves up. Everyone lay down where he found himself and slept, though the imaginative shouted, cried horrors, and gesticulated in their sleep.

Catherine Black was now working on the Somme, and was in charge of a ward for shell-shocked officers. Psychological trauma, she believed,

> … was one of the saddest conditions produced by modern warfare … At first sight most of my patients appeared to have little or nothing the matter with them, but at night the cheerful ward became a place of torment, with the occupant of every bed tossing and turning and moaning in a hell of memories let loose.

She felt professionally inadequate while nursing the shell-shocked cases:

There was so little one could do to help them ... no two shell-shocked cases were ever the same, and one man would respond favourably to treatment that would be disastrous for another. Rest was the one thing that all of them most urgently needed, and so for the first week or ten days we gave them opiates and tried to build up their general health. After that we could study each individual case and deal with it as best we could. It was work that demanded endless patience, for results were slow and you could only go a step at a time and hope for the best.

The wounds of the mind required time, patience, rest and understanding, but treatment such as this was perceived by some senior officers as a 'luxury' they were not prepared to sanction. In August, strict instructions were issued relating to the evacuation of shell-shocked cases. The ferocity of the battle being waged on the Somme, with its rising attrition rates, demanded that 'wastage' due to psychological injury was not to be tolerated unless 'there are definite lesions and symptoms which require prolonged hospital treatment.'

So, men were conserved, in body at least, to feed the appetite of the guns. By now, 200,000 British and Dominion troops had been killed or wounded. Winston Churchill expressed his dismay at the futility of the deaths:

I view with the utmost pain, this terrible killing of our troops. We have not gained in a month's fighting as much ground as we were expected to gain in the first two hours. We have not advanced two miles in a direct line at any point.

Disquiet at the experience and fighting capabilities of the new drafts being sent out to France was expressed by one officer:

A large number had been attested only six weeks before they came to us, so unready had the War Office been to replace the losses properly. What was called training hardly amounted to a 'lick and a promise', it did not fit the men to take part in any operation. They had fired only five rounds of ball cartridge; many of them did not know how to load and unload a rifle, to fix and unfix a bayonet.

Was it morally correct to send such inexperienced troops into battle? If men with at least one year's training were struggling to take and hold a line, what could such novices realistically achieve? Many of those inexperienced men died within weeks of joining the army. Others, 'blooded' on the Somme, went on to fight, or die, in future campaigns.

September saw a little more success for the allies when the heavily defended villages of Guillemont and Ginchy were taken from the Germans. For two months, British and Dominion troops were thrown at the small French hamlets. The names of Guillemont and Ginchy and their surrounding woods became bywords for wholesale slaughter. In that charnel house, the evidence of the brutality and density of fighting was witnessed by Father William Doyle as he advanced with the 8th Royal Irish Fusiliers towards Leuze Wood.

> The first part of our journey lay through a narrow trench, the floor of which consisted of deep thick mud, and the bodies of dead men trodden under foot. It was horrible beyond description, but there was no help for it, and on those half rotten corpses of our brave men we marched in silence, everyone busy with their own thoughts. Half an hour of this brought us out on the open into the middle of the battlefield of some days previous … The dead lay there, stiff and stark, with open staring eyes, just as they had fallen. Good God, such a sight, I had tried to prepare myself for this. Some lay as if they were sleeping quietly, others had died in agony, or had the life crushed out of them by mortal fear, while the whole ground, every foot of it, was littered with heads or limbs or pieces of human body.

By November, as the Somme offensive drew to an end, it was claimed that the military operations in Picardy had cost the British and Dominion Forces 419,000 casualties, 54,550 of whom were in Casualty Clearing Stations and hospitals in France. Thousands more had been shipped back to Britain and were now in the specially designated military hospitals throughout Britain and Ireland. The women of Britain, who in 1914 and 1915 had been so eager to nurse the sick and wounded, now had ample opportunity to step forward and do their bit – but they didn't. The *Sheffield Daily Telegraph* reported:

> A number of Society girls who, earlier in the War, deserted homes in Mayfair and Belgravia for hospital wards, seem to have tired of the discipline there and returned to their old pursuits. Lunch time sees them in their accustomed places at the Carlton grill room or the Ritz.

The cost of the Somme battles was now obvious to everyone. In a letter to the *Daily Telegraph* written in the final month of the Somme campaign, Lord Lansdowne questioned the way the war was being prosecuted.

> We are slowly but surely killing off the best of the male population of these islands. Can we afford to go on paying the same sort of price for the same sort of gain?

From July to November, in the battles for Albert, Bazentin Ridge, Delville Wood, Pozieres Ridge, Guillemont, Ginchy, Flers-Courcelette, Morval, Thiepval, Transloy Ridge and Ancre Heights, the British and Dominion Forces sustained approximately 2,910 casualties per day. The total Somme casualties were estimated at 419,000 over 144 days of fighting. The policy entrusted to Douglas Haig of 'avoiding heavy losses and wastage,' lay shattered like the minds and bodies of thousands of men. Philip Gibbs summed up the tragedy of the Somme battles.

> There was a great carving of human flesh which was of our boyhood, while the old men directed their sacrifice, and the profiteers grew rich, and the fires of hate were stoked up at patriotic banquets and in editorial chairs.

After ten months of fighting the French held Verdun but the cost to La Patrie, according to France's Official War History, was 377,231 casualties of which 162,308 were killed or missing.

On the Home Front, the *British Journal of Nursing* fulminated about the government's response to the problem of the shortage of nurses.

> Last week we were once more startled by a professional bomb. A committee had been quietly engineered, and appointed by the Secretary of State for War, to enquire into the present shortage of nurses in military hospitals at home and abroad, and to make recommendations on how to augment the supply – composed of seven men and one untrained woman – a Committee to deal with the economic conditions of the Nursing Profession and not one trained nurse upon it!

The members of the Committee were Mr W. Bridgman MP, who acted as Chairman, Viscount Knutsford, Sir Frederick Treves, the Honorable Francis Curzon, Mrs Furse, Commander-in Chief of the British Red Cross Society VAD Department, Captain Harold Boulton, and Mr E. W. Morris. The absence of trained nurses on the committee was surely a perfectly legitimate grievance to be raised by the trained nurses. A letter from the Council of the College of Nursing to the Secretary of State for War wasted no time in expressing displeasure and disappointment at the exclusion of professionally trained nurses from the Supply of Nurses Committee.

> Sir,
> I beg to inform you that the Council of the College of Nursing met this afternoon to discuss the recent appointment of the Committee … The Council wish respectfully to bring to your notice the following conclusions at which they unanimously arrived.
>
> - That the Nursing profession has fully responded to all the calls that have been made upon it since the outbreak of war, and that it may therefore be

a question whether the appointment of such a Committee is either necessary or opportune.

- That the Committee as announced is not such as to command the confidence of the Nursing profession.

- That the trained Nurses of the country look upon the appointment of the Committee as a slight upon the efforts and sacrifices which they have willingly made to fulfil the requirements imposed upon the Nursing Staffs of military and civil hospitals during the war.

- That the Matrons of the civil hospitals throughout the country have shown their willingness to assist the Matrons-in-Chief and the Army Nursing Board in every way and resent the appointment of a wholly unprofessional Committee to deal with this most important subject.

In this connection it may be pointed out that the Army Nursing was set up by Royal Warrant 'to act as advisers to HM Secretary of State in all matters pertaining to Military Nursing in times of peace and war.'

The Council desires to add that they have no hesitation in saying that any proposals emanating from the Army Nursing Board would receive the cordial support of the Matrons and of the profession at large. In view of these facts, the Council begs that further action with this Committee may be suspended, until the matter has had fuller consideration.

The memory of *British Journal of Nursing* writers was selective regarding the supply of nurses. At the beginning of the year it had proclaimed: 'While so many nurses with excellent certificates are available, there is no excuse for employing persons with lower qualifications.' Where were the 'many' nurses with excellent qualifications? They certainly were not evident to the War Office, which was forced to issue a statement to the press about the 'misunderstanding' which had arisen over the Government's intention to deal with the shortage of nurses:

Some misunderstanding seems to have arisen as to the function of the Committee recently appointed by the Secretary of State for War to consider the question of the supply of nurses. It was intended that the duties of the Committee should be to collect statistics as to the number of nurses available, trained and untrained, and to submit suggestions for the consideration of the War Office and Army Nursing Board.

But it has been represented to the Secretary of State for War by the chairman of the Committee that it will be impossible to make such an examination of the statistics collected as will satisfactorily support any recommendation they may make without the assistance, as members of the Committee, of representatives of the Army Nursing Boards and some of the large general hospitals. The Secretary of State for War has therefore decided to add to the Committee certain representatives of those interested. The names will be announced in the Press as soon as the selection has been made and the invitation accepted.

In modern parlance this was clearly a U-turn as they were now forced to invite representatives of trained nurses to join the Committee. The *British Journal of Nursing* could not resist reminding the government that:

> In 1914 we suggested to the War Office that an expert committee should be appointed ... we hope nothing will prevent the Secretary of State for War appointing a really representative committee which will be able to give him sound and practical advice on the matter. When we hear of nurses on duty from 7 a.m. to 12 p.m., of the backs of a dozen sick men being washed in the same water, of overstrained matrons reprimanding the nursing staff before the patients, of patients set to do manual work for which they are not fit, of squabbles, rows, and lack of discipline amongst all classes of officials, it is high time that something should be done to relieve the tension.

Although six representatives of trained nurses were invited to join the Committee, the farce continued. On 7 October, the Irish Nurses Association wrote to the Secretary of State for War that, 'no representative for Ireland has been appointed to serve on the Committee. We presume that this is an oversight which will be rectified at an early date!' On 18 October a representative of the Irish Nurses Association secured a place on the SNC. On 20 October, the Secretary for the Joint VAD Committee for Ireland wrote to the Secretary of War Office requesting that a representative of the VAD serve on the Committee. It was met with the following swift response by letter:

> ... that in response to an appeal from the Irish Nurses Association they invited that association to select a representative to serve on the Committee. Your Committee will thus see that representation from Ireland is already provided for. I am to add that Mrs Furse, the Commandant-in-Chief of the Joint Women's VAD Department, is already a member of the Committee.

The shortage of nurses was not surprising. By 1916 the reality of nursing the sick and wounded held none of the glamour and excitement that many women envisaged at the start of the war. On the Western Front, the war was beginning to exact a heavy death and sickness toll on the relatively small number of trained nurses. Nurses were being sent back to Britain and Ireland with debilitating conditions such as strokes, ulcerative colitis, heart disease, tuberculosis, rheumatoid arthritis, cancer, osteomylitis and kidney failure. Several more cases of neurasthenia and 'debility' were diagnosed in nursing staff who were transported back home to the care of their families. There were 43 deaths in the nursing ranks; 24 sisters, 14 staff-nurses, 3 VAD nurses and 2 probationers. The main causes of death were septicaemia, dysentery, pneumonia, meningitis, tuberculosis, and one accidental drowning.

**The Home Front: wounded men convalescing after the Somme Battles, wearing their distinctive 'Blighty' blue hospital uniform.**

As Christmas approached there was little thought for festivities. The Somme battles had left far too many families bereft of fathers, sons, brothers, uncles and cousins. There were also, of course, 43 families mourning the loss of their women; women who had unselfishly gone to care for the sick and wounded and tragically lost their own lives in the process. The casualty lists printed in newspapers and the growing number of sick and wounded arriving back in Britain and Ireland were a constant reminder that patriotism came at a very high price.

In Liverpool, an innovative scheme carried out by a band of volunteer workers allowed some sick and wounded men from different parts of Britain and Ireland to spend Christmas with their families. A house rented for the 'Duration of the War', or as long as it was needed, was established as a family hostel near the First Western General Hospital at Fazakerley. The hostel could accommodate 17 people and the hospitality was free. Families able to do so were asked to make a small donation. To ensure the upkeep of this hostel a pamphlet describing the value of the hostel and the need for ongoing financial support was circulated to potential benefactors and the public:

As you know, wounded men are drafted to Fazakerley Hospital whose homes are situated in various parts of the country. The convenience of a hostel to the wife or mother who is not endowed with this world's goods, but who is called upon to make a long journey, will appeal to you very strongly. It enables many a sorrowing woman to stay by the bedside of perhaps a mortally wounded husband or son, affording them both the comfort of each other's presence in their sad trouble … Please help us succour the strangers within our gates. They have suffered much for us.

On 23 December, the editorial of the *British Journal of Nursing* was more conciliatory and reflective, but it could only muster a few 'inspirational' words for the readership.

The shadow of war lies chill across the Christmas season … Keep cheerful should be in the hearts and on the lips of all of us, for private troubles must now, more than ever, be secondary to public duty …

The editorial concluded with a familiar Christmas greeting:

To all our readers, and very especially to all such brave souls, we wish a Happy Christmas.

**Christmas 1916 at George V Military Hospital, Dublin. Note the absence of hospital uniforms. Since the Easter Rising, it had become 'difficult' for a southern Irishman to be seen in a uniform of the British Army.**

## Chapter VII

## *'Pack up your Troubles'*

# Spirituality, Inspiration and Esprit de Corps 1917

By 1917, David Lloyd George had become Prime Minister, and in spite of the 1916 carnage on the Somme, Douglas Haig had been promoted to the rank of Field Marshal. The distinction of 'war wounded' was accorded to thousands of wounded men, many of whom now required artificial, arms, legs and eyes; there were also, of course, the disfigured, the paralysed and the shell shocked. In recognition of their war-acquired wounds they were given a silver badge bearing the Imperial cipher surmounted by a crown, with the inscription 'For King and Empire Services Rendered'.

Lord Lansdowne had written to the *Daily Telegraph* in November 1916 raising his concerns about the way the war was being prosecuted. By early 1917 he was in a position to claim that a number of officers serving at the front had 'welcomed' his letter. Nevertheless, it evidently bore no weight at the War Office and the allied offensive continued into 1917. However, the medical and nursing services wasted no time incorporating into the casualty treatment and evacuation plans valuable lessons learned from the Somme campaign. More accommodation and better shelter were to be provided for Regimental Aid Posts and Advanced Dressing Stations; relay posts for stretcher-bearers were to be established every 1,000 yards and there was to be a more organised use of the various forms of transportation. Casualty Clearing Stations were to be formed into two or three groups so that admissions could be rotated. Special units were established to deal with abdominal wounds, skin conditions, and nervous disorders and a scheme for the provision of 'crisis' beds was established.

On 9 April 1917, after a five-day, 2,800-gun preliminary bombardment, the British and Dominion forces launched their spring offensive at Arras. In 1916, a similar tactic had been carried out with disastrous consequences in advance of the 1 July assault – the element of surprise had gone and the Germans had been prepared for the attack. Lessons had not been learned and military history repeated itself when between 9 April and 14 April the British and Dominion forces sustained terrible losses for relatively small gains.

The Canadian Corps successfully took the long-contested stronghold of Vimy Ridge – at a cost of 14,000 casualties. It was claimed that the capture of the ridge 'marked a point in Canada's progress towards nationhood in the sense that its army had won a great battle.'

By the spring of 1917, Sister Luard had left the hospital trains and was now in charge of a casualty clearing station near Arras. The winter of 1916–1917 was extremely severe, which meant the movement of casualties was hampered. Wounded men could lie in the bitter cold for days before being moved on to Casualty Clearing Stations or Base Hospitals. For some, the delay in treatment secured their fate. According to Sister Luard, between 23 April and 27 April, she and her colleagues were, 'hard at it again':

Monday 23rd: The Director of Medical Services came to ask me for a Sister to go up to a new Abdominal Special Hospital with a Field Ambulance at a place farther up; out of shell range, but overlooking the whole battlefield … This new abdominal stunt is making a difference already – it ought to save many lives. A captain of the Yorks had his leg off yesterday and makes less of it than some people with a toe-nail off. The glorious boy with the broken back is lying on his back now; he doesn't know about it and says he's all right, only his back is a little stiff and aching. Some of the men say they were picked up and looked after by Germans, so we are being extra kind to the Germans this time. There is in hospitals an understood arrangement that all Germans (except when their lives depend on immediate attention) should wait till the last British has been attended to, for dressings, operations, food, blankets, etc. It is only kept up in a very half-hearted way and is generally broken by the MOs, who are most emphatic about it in theory!

Tuesday 24th: It has been a pretty sad day, twelve funerals, including four officers, all fine, brave men. The spine boy has found out what is the matter with him and is quite cheery about it; told me to tell his mother he had Holy Communion this morning and that she was not to worry about him … One mother wrote thanking me for writing to tell her about her son, but 'it would relieve the news somewhat if she knew which son it was, as she has three sons in France.' The people who have been coming in all day are the left-outs in German dug-outs since Monday, starved, cold, and by some miracle still alive, but not much more. This last 300 has taken sixteen hours to come in.

Thursday 26th: The officer boy with the fractured spine isn't going to die yet; though the CO gave him twenty-four hours days ago. I got the Colonel to put him on the evacuation list tonight to give him a chance to get X-rayed at the base and perhaps recover. Icy cold wind all day. We shall be due to take-in tomorrow morning, the first that come back from Over the Top.

Friday 27th: The attack came off all right, but he (as the enemy is frequently called in these parts and in the communiqués) didn't wait for it! He has gone back another five miles, so all those hundreds of our casualties are saved and there's nothing doing. My dear little resuscitated Suffolk boy got gas gangrene above the amputation and died this afternoon, and the other boy has had to have the other leg off now. In one ward there's hardly a man with two legs; and when one Boche made a noise when he was being dressed, there was a chorus of encouragement from the British beds, 'Hold on, Fritz; soon be done – be all right in a minute,' regardless of any difficulty in language! The boy wounded in the spine with total paralysis below the chest was safely taken to the train this evening. When I told him he was going down to be X-rayed, he said, 'That'll be better than lying on my back all my life,' and his eyes filled with tears. All these days he has never said one word of complaint or self-pity, though he knew his probable fate from the second day. An orderly who has been running the marquee of fifty stretcher-cases without a sister, has gone sick with trench fever. He leads one of the most Christ-like lives I've ever seen; there is no other word for his selfless devotion, though he is comic beyond words in speech and appearance!

Saturday night 27th: I didn't mean to write tonight, as fourteen hours a day every day with these wonderful smashed-up soldiers doesn't leave much over at bed-time. They make you feel proud of belonging to the same race. There's a handsome young Scot with one leg off who asked me last night to take his socks off. I took the one off. 'Have you taken the other off, too?' he asked. 'Yes,' I said guiltily, 'they're both off now.' Next day Sister told me he knew his leg was off, but he didn't. Tonight he said, 'My feet are hot.' 'Yes' I said, 'especially the one you haven't got, I suppose?' (It always is the one they feel most.) 'Have I got but one?' he said. I was covered with confusion. 'Ah, well, I see by what ye say I've got but one, but it's no matter. I feel a pain in them whiles, but I can smile between the pains. I've got two daughters and a wee son I've never seen. I know what I'll do when I do see them. Don't I know?' (And I'm afraid he's in for gas gangrene and may not see them). Then he looked round at all the stumps and splints and heads and said, 'Seems a pity nearly everyone has got to get like this before Peace is declared.'

By 1917, against the backdrop of continued carnage, inhuman combat conditions and military blunders, the men and women serving on the Western Front had found a variety of ways to accommodate the intensity of their feelings and prevent breakdown of their physical and mental health. The often appalling conditions in which they fought, worked and lived were confronted and negotiated by means of a variety of belief and support systems. In the midst of the war's collective misery, inspiring and spiritual experiences gave soldiers and nurses the fortitude to face the horrors and terrors of long and bloody campaigns, and they were encouraged and strengthened by religion, humour, literature, artefacts, lucky charms, music, compassionate interactions with animals, and esprit de corps. On the other hand, fear, despair, revulsion, anger, frustration and boredom found companionship in alcohol, tobacco, sex and drugs.

Religion, religious artefacts and lucky charms appear to have helped sustain soldiers and nurses, many of whom were morally, ethically and emotionally challenged by their involvement in war. The war correspondent, Michael MacDonagh reported that the use of religious objects or talismans had become commonplace to ward off death and injury during battle.

> The wearing of religious emblems by soldiers of the British Army is much talked of by doctors and nurses in military hospitals in France and at home. When wounded soldiers are undressed be they non-Catholic or Catholic – the discovery is frequently made of medals or scapulars worn around their necks, or sacred badges stitched inside their tunics. It is the psychological phenomenon of much interest for the light it throws upon human nature in the ordeal of war.

MacDonagh further reported enormous sales of a special charm, 'Touchwood', specifically designed for soldiers:

> 'Touchwood' is a tiny imp, mainly head, made of oak, surmounted by a khaki service cap, and with odd, sparkling eyes as if always on the alert to see and avert danger. The designer, Mr. H. Brandon, states that he has sold 1,250,000 of this charm since the war broke out. Beads, medals and scapulars are venerated, and proudly displayed over their tunics – often, too, rosary beads are seen to be twisted round rifle barrels.

Rowland Feilding, commanding the 1st Battalion, Connaught Rangers, observed the effect that religious artefacts could have on Catholics as well as non-Catholics. Following the presentation to his battalion of small crucifixes, which had been sent out as gifts from his wife, and blessed by the Pope, he wrote:

> The ceremony of presenting your crucifixes was performed this morning. All of the battalion that was available – between 600 and 700 – marched in sunshine to the Parish Church of Locre, led by the regimental pipes and drums... When mass was over, the priest asked all but the two Generals

and the Connaught Rangers to leave the church, and he then presented the crucifixes; first to the Generals; then to the Guard of Honour; then to the officers and men of the battalion, all of whom kissed them as they received them, and have, I believe, since hung them round their necks. One of my non-Catholic Company Commanders asked if he might take a crucifix. He told me later that it was the most impressive ceremony he had ever seen: and I may admit that the devout reverence of these soldiers, as they filed up towards the altar, affected me too, very deeply.

A nursing sister at a Base Hospital in Belgium wrote of the destruction of churches and religious objects, but as she visited the Church of St Elisabeth, which had been spared she noted:

The little Church of St. Elisabeth stands among the grey dunes looking out on the silvery sea ... It is a plain wooden structure put together by the soldiers themselves, and you will notice that they have hung the great black wooden Cross bearing the piteous Christ on the wall furthest away from the German guns ... Enter and you will see that the Church is full of spectral forms. Can it be that these phantom shapes gleaming faintly in the blueness of the twilight, are the ghosts of the innocent victims who have lost their lives and who have come together to mourn the tragedy of Belgium? Look again, and you will see that this little church is a sanctuary, full of poignant memories of what has been. This is the home for the crucifixes, the statues, the holy things from the bombarded churches in the neighbourhood. There hangs a great broken crucifix found unaccountably in the trenches at Pervyse, a poor, battered St. Lawrence, and a less maimed St Christopher from Nieuport ... That fragment of masonry in the corner is all that is left of the altar at Avchapelle, and most of those brass candlesticks huddled up together once stood upon it. You may, if you choose, say your prayers beside the Madonna from Ramskapelle, from whose tender arms the Child has been torn by a fragment of shell and splintered into a thousand pieces. She stands there with Her piteous empty arms outstretched, and another mother, mourning her only son has crept into the Church and knelt down beside Her for comfort and sympathy in her loss ...

The Army Chaplains' Department did much to bring religious and moral strength to combatants and to succour the fragile and distraught. It was not possible, however, for the Chaplains' Department to deal with all the religious denominations serving in the British, Dominion and Allied Forces. Army chaplains, affectionately known as padres, attended to men's needs when and where possible. It was noted that:

The fire and support trenches offer chaplains golden opportunities. With the exception of the sentries on duty, all the men are either resting in dug-outs and shelters, or repairing their own portion of the trench. Having ample time for conversation they eagerly welcome and appreciate a chaplain's visit.

It is perhaps no exaggeration to say that the surest way for a chaplain to become popular with both officers and men is to be frequently with them in the firing line. These visits are not paid for without incurring personal risk, but the standing gained by so doing is well worth the venture.

Throughout the duration of the war, 'personal risk' cost 179 padres their lives; they were killed in action or died of their wounds. Three were awarded the VC. While ministers and priests were able to give religious or spiritual comfort, meaningful gestures were important. A padre posted to a Scottish Regiment observed the reactions, and actions, of men when they discovered their much loved senior officer was dead.

The officers and men were a great lot. We had one Major who was over six feet in height and broad with it, the men nicknamed him 'MacDuff'. What a man he was – the men worshipped him. On a raiding party one night the Major received a wound to his abdomen and it was obvious the end was near. I shall never forget that night. I went round the posts. Men called out, 'Padre, MacDuff's no deid! He's no deid!' More than one wept that night. We buried him at Montescourt. The raiding party made a coffin out of biscuit-box wood and lined it with tinfoil.

Because of the huge number of deaths, coffins were impractical and soldiers were generally wrapped in their army blanket for burial; anything hand-made was a labour of love and deep respect.

The writer stretcher-bearer, Patrick McGill, strongly believed that the brutality of war needed to be balanced with compassion and a right to exercise spiritual or religious beliefs. Having entered an enemy trench taken by his regiment, he came across a dying German, his right arm almost severed at the shoulder.

I entered and gazed at him. There was a look of mute appeal in his eyes, and for some reason I felt ashamed of myself for having intruded on the privacy of a dying man. There comes a time when man on the field of battle should be left alone to his own thoughts. I loosened my water bottle from its holder and by sign inquired if he wanted a drink. He nodded and I placed the bottle on his lips. I'd taken my bottle of morphine tablets from my pocket and explained to him as well as I was able what the bottle contained, and he permitted me to place two under his tongue. When rummaging in my pocket I happened to bring out my rosary beads and he noticed them. He spoke and I guessed that he was inquiring if I was a Catholic. I nodded to assent. He fumbled with his left hand in his tunic pocket and brought out a little mud-stained booklet and handed it to me. I noticed that the volume was a prayer book. By his signs I concluded that he wanted me to keep it. I attempted to leave, but he called me back and pointed to his trousers pocket as if he wanted me to bring something out of it. I could see that he required me to do something further for him. Then raising his left hand with difficulty (I now saw that blood was flowing down the wrist) he pointed at his tunic pocket, a piece of string and a photo were all that the pocket contained. The photograph showed a man, whom I saw was the soldier, a woman and a little child seated at a table. I'd put it in his hand and with brilliant eyes and set teeth he raised his head to look at it – I went outside.

MacGill goes on to describe the battlefield and the need for the dying to connect with a source which would give them strength or succour. He came across one dead German who, in the last throes of death, had apparently been attempting to connect with his family.

I came across a crumpled figure of a man in grey, dead in the shell-crater. One arm was bent under him and the other stretched forward almost touching a photograph of a woman and three little children. I placed the photograph under the edge of the man's tunic.

Near him lay another Bavarian, an old man, deeply wrinkled and white haired, and wounded through the chest. He was trembling all over like a wounded bird, but his eyes were calm and they looked beyond the tumult and turmoil of the battlefield into some secret world that only the dying can see. A rosary was in the man's hand and his lips were mumbling something: he was telling his beads.

Not every serving soldier came from a Judeo-Christian background or was supported by religious belief and there was considerable diversity of culture and religion among men who came from all parts of The British Empire. In response to an article published in the *British Journal of Nursing* on nursing and cultural beliefs, a nursing sister wrote:

I was glad to see that you drew attention to the need for nurses to cultivate the spirit of wisdom and understanding. We have to deal with patients of such diversity of views, race and religion so that our sympathies should be as broad as the sea. The sick man carried out of bed in a warm hospital to die on snow-covered ground found freedom. He was in the act of dying, and nothing mattered except that he should die as easily as possible and that he was able to do so because someone saw him and understood that according to his Eastern Creed he should die on Mother Earth.

In hospital, recovering from his wounds, a Lieutenant supported a decision made by his senior officer that there should be no segregation on the grounds of rank or religious beliefs.

> Never was a wiser decision made by our late, loved Commanding Officer when it was decided that there should be no segregation or distinction between patients. The war has brought men from the uttermost parts of the Empire into closer touch than ever before, allowed them to see their own defects, and appreciate the good qualities in others. For their countries and life interests have proved the basis of many a conversation, besides best and greatest of all being the means of cementing life friendships.

While religious beliefs and spiritual experiences greatly supported many soldiers and nurses, small gifts could uplift or encourage dispirited men. For example, Mrs Henry Lee from Llandrindod sent lavender bags for the sick and wounded prompting an army chaplain serving at the Front to ask her for 30,000 more.

> I wish you could see how much the dainty little lavender bags mean to most of the wounded … I knew that some would appreciate them, but I had no idea that they would appeal, as they do, to nearly all … The wards are quite fragrant to-day, and last night at least one man passed away with his little bag tightly clasped in his hand … I so much wish you could see the pleasure and comfort they give. Nearly every badly wounded and sick patient has a lavender bag pinned to his pillow (they ask the nurses to pin them on), and most of those who are evacuated to Base Hospitals are careful to take the little bag with them.

Lady Smith-Dorrian's Hospital Bag Fund met with equal success. The bags were made so that the sick or wounded could keep their personal possessions with them while in hospital. In a published report, Lady Smith-Dorrian claimed that, from October 1916 to June 1917, 'thanks to the generous support of 12,000 contributors' she was able to respond to all the demands for Hospital Bags for the sick and wounded.

> That the demands are not small is indicated in that since the beginning of the year the monthly average sent to the Front has been 106,000, and further, that the total sent since the fund was started is within a few hundreds of two million … The medical authorities and officers and men themselves are loud in praise of the value of the Bags and have come to regard them as a necessity.

Religious, spiritual and welfare needs were further catered for by the Young Men's Christian Association (YMCA) and the Salvation Army. Both organisations concerned themselves with social and welfare benefits for the troops and dealt with queries regarding soldiers missing in action and prisoners of war. On the Home and Western Front, huts, canteens and marquees were set up to supply hot refreshments, reading rooms, games rooms, religious services and concerts. The YMCA facilities offered free writing paper and envelopes and initiated the 'Snapshot League' when it enrolled 11,000 amateur photographers to take pictures of the families and friends of soldiers and sailors.

The men were supplied with application forms which they completed, specifying who they wished to be photographed – wife, children, parents or other loved ones. The forms were returned to the YMCA in London, forwarded to the nearest volunteer photographer and the photographs were then dispatched in special waterproof envelopes; 500,000 photographs were sent out to the Western Front or elsewhere. The YMCA also organised free legal advice for non-commissioned officers and soldiers; this advice was confined to civil matters and was given by barristers and solicitors on active service.

Music played an important role, helping to sustain individual and troop morale. It was claimed that thousands of copies of the penny edition of *Camp Songs* were sold. It contained a collection of patriotic, humorous and sentimental songs, and prompted the 'sing-along' or the 'sing-song' in the YMCA huts and canteens, usually equipped with a piano. Singing old and new songs, particularly their own compositions and renditions, uplifted spirits and inspired hesitant men as they marched down the line. The men sang in their trenches, billets, estaminets, troop ships and trains, on route marches, at impromptu and organised concerts, and in hospital beds. The patriotic songs composed at the outbreak of war, and sung with enthusiasm and gusto – 'We Don't Want to Lose You', 'Keep the Home Fires Burning', 'Pack up Your Troubles in Your Old Kit Bag' – soon gave way to more cynical renditions and compositions such as, 'My Little Wet Hole In The Trench', 'Hanging on the Old Barbed Wire', 'That Shit Shute'.

Concert parties were well attended and much appreciated. They were considered invaluable in raising troop morale, and gave men a psychological respite from the dangers of the trenches and the boredom of billets. Max Plowman claimed that a battalion on rest wants 'a company canteen, a reading and writing room with games, inter-platoon and inter-company football matches, musical instruments, a gramophone, and company concerts at least once a week.' Lena Ashwell, a well-known actress and active suffragist who had trained at the Royal Academy of Music, combined her various talents to produce concert parties for the troops, usually held in YMCA huts. Ashwell remembers the first concert party, held in a new Cinema Hut.

> The wooden hut was packed to suffocation … the men had been waiting for hours and smoking incessantly, and the fog of smoke and the heat within the hut was a tremendous contrast to the cold, rain and mud … Ivor Novello, who was one of the party, had just written 'Keep the Home Fires Burning', and when he sang it, the men seemed to drink it in at once and instantly sang the chorus, and as we drove away at the end of the concert, in the dark and rain and mud, from all parts of the camp one could hear the refrain of the chorus.

The concert party was a welcome relief for nurses as well as the men, and some nursing sisters appreciated the therapeutic value music had for their patients. Lena Ashwell performed in hospitals, YMCA huts and concert halls and adapted her concert party's repartee to suit the needs and wishes of the sick and wounded. A nurse wrote in a letter home about how, after a concert held in the orderly room:

> … those kind people came into each ward and sang softly with no accompaniment to the men who were well enough to listen, and the little Canadian storyteller told stories to each man in turn as he was having his dressings done. The result was that instead of being a suffering mass of humanity, the men were happy and amused through the whole of the time that is usually so awful.

According to Miss Ashwell:

> It is only natural that hospital patients should enjoy most what they can appreciate with the least effort, and it can be therefore readily understood that the ballad-singer, and above all the instrumentalist, should be the most popular in the hospital. The last movement of the Mendelssohn Concerto and the Intermezzo of the Cavalleria Rusticana, Handel's 'Largo' were always much loved in hospital.
>
> When the nursing sister would have kept a Serious Case Ward sacred and undisturbed, the men asked that some music might come into them. Literally, music is what they crave for, even when they are dying. On one occasion there was a man in very great pain; his tense face strained and infinitely weary, he was waiting for the music to start. When the violinist passed him he said, 'Give us something nippy, Miss.' She went up to the top of the room and played the gayest tune she knew, but when she looked for his face at the end of it, she saw he had passed on to the Great Unknown while she was playing.

**Divisional and Battalion concert parties were held where the men staged their own shows. Inevitably, a Tommy dressed up as a nurse. Also organised were Divisional sports meetings, boxing tournaments, horse shows, football and cricket matches.**

While there was a resonance in emotive lyrics and instrumentals, and men could be uplifted and encouraged by them, it would appear that, as in earlier times, the War Pipes (bagpipes) had the most profound influence on men. After the 1745 Rebellion, the pipes were outlawed in Scotland and classed as 'instruments of war' because of the inspirational effect they had on clansmen. In Scottish, and Irish regiments, the emotional effect of bagpipes was well known and understood by officers and men alike. Two pipers witnessing the first gas attack at Ypres in 1915 acted spontaneously in trying to rally the troops. According to their officer:

> Two of the battalion pipers who were acting as stretcher-bearers saw the situation. In a moment, dropping their stretcher they made for the dug-out and emerged a second later with their pipes. They sprang on to the parapet, and charged forward. Fierce and terrible the wild notes left in the air ... after fifteen yards the pipes ceased; the two pipers, choked and suffocated with the gas fumes; they staggered and fell.

Pipers became legendary, continuing to play in the midst of battle or after they were wounded. During one of the Somme battles an officer of the Black Watch recalled that:

> The heroism of the piper was splendid. In spite of murderous fire a Seaforth piper dashed forward in front of the line and started playing

'Cabar Feidh'. The effect was instantaneous – the sorely pressed men braced themselves together and charged forward. The Germans soon got to realise the value of the pipes and tried to pick off the pipers'.

Months later, a directive was sent out from GCHQ banning pipers from advancing with their companies. One officer noted: 'The edict against pipers playing their companies into action fretted many a piper throughout the service and was disregarded whenever an opportunity offered.' In 1917, during a bombing raid at Arras, pipers Whitelaw and McGurk defied the order and piped their comrades over the parapet and into 'No Man's Land.' According to their officer, 'it was a spectacle that thrilled all beholders of other battalions in the vicinity.'

Sister Peterkin's Scottish identity and the fondness she felt for the Scottish troops helped her cope with the vagaries of war and, after an evening with soldiers from different Scottish regiments, she wrote:

We had a Scottish concert last night. A soldier from the Black Watch danced the Highland Fling accompanied by a pipe major on the bagpipes, they did really well ... I got a box of cigarettes from the 10th Royal Scots!

Creative writing allowed men and women to express themselves and to describe the horrors of war without the fear of censorship. Poetry was a popular medium. At the beginning of the war, poetry was pastoral and romantic, and the propagandists used it to convey bravery and patriotism. By 1915, the perceived romanticism in sending men off to war became questionable and Charles Sorley, a soldier-poet, expressed his rising distaste for the war when he wrote his last poem, 'When you see millions of the mouthless dead' – Captain Charles Sorley was only twenty years of age when he was killed in action at the Battle of Loos.

From 1916 onwards, a prolific amount of poetry emerged from the Western Front; for some, there was a need to rationalise the slaughter which they believed was caused by military incompetence. Much of the poetry which emerged from combat experience dealt with spirituality, brotherhood, God, insanity, disability, animals and nature.

For the benefit of the public, alienated from the war and receiving sanitised reports on its conduct, the soldier poets wrote with first-hand experience about what was happening to the minds and bodies of fathers, sons and brothers. Some of the most telling war poetry went unpublished; many men and women writing about their experiences viewed their efforts as amateurish and kept the poems as private recollections, never to be read by the public. Front line and hospital poetry was humorous or sentimental and quite often featured nurses.

## Hold On!

She's weary and faint, and her brain is like lead
She'd barter her leave for an hour on her bed
Her heart is one ache, but no tear will she shed
Hold on!

The stretchers are coming in – rows upon rows
And the air is sick with the reek that she knows;
Will she falter or flinch when her care is for those
Hold on!

And she who is British will stick it no fear!
O game little Sister I know you my dear!

## My Little Irish Nurse

She came to me so cheery kind,
Her steps so swift and light,
Her strong, warm hands drove fear away,
and soothed me in the night.
Her voice is like the whisperings
The angels send to earth.
Her presence is a peace a rest
My little Irish Nurse!

Her dark eyes hold a Faith that looks
From a soul God knows is His.
Life's daily task fulfil a round
Of beauty, mirroring this.
O, Service sacred gift to heal
An aching universe!
'Tis hands like yours lift the cooling draught
My little Irish nurse!

Trench journalism was rife and was yet another form of creative writing that allowed the men to abandon army etiquette and rank. The purpose of trench journals was to amuse, criticise and grouse. The British and Dominion Forces produced over one hundred journals with the titles reflecting many of the sentiments and situations – *The Dead Horse Corner Gazette, The Rum Issue, Mules Monthly, The Whizz Bang, The Iodine Chronicle, The Poultice,* and *The Dug Out Despatch.*

*The Times Literary Supplement* described the content of the journals as 'miscellanies of personal chaff, old Service jokes, crude parodies, rude drawings, spoof examination papers and bogus advertisements.' Whatever their content, they provided much needed light relief from the brutality of war and they provided a platform for satirising those who brought them into the war and who kept and controlled them within it.

Creative writing was just as important to nurses as it was to the men of the British and Dominion forces. The active service life of nurses was detailed in their own poems and stories and one sister, who had gone out with the original expeditionary force in 1914, composed a poem about what camp life was like in the early months of the war.

### Camp Life

Perhaps you'd like to hear about
The Sister's life in camp
And how we lived and how we slept
In heat, or cold, or damp

The days were very hot at first
The nights were deadly cold
We went to bed in jerseys
And we looked like Knights of Old

The Batman called us in the morn
A dixie full of tea
He pushed inside the tent at seven
And very glad were we!

It warmed us up like nothing else
And then we washed and dressed
We stole what privacy we could
And did without the rest!

They're lots of things that I could write
Enough to fill a book
But when I told a Sister this
She gave a nervous look

She seemed afraid that I should not
Display sufficient tact
But truth with me is everything
And all I write is fact!

Many articles and essays detailing active service got past the censor and were submitted to professional, church and ladies' journals.

Autograph books were extremely fashionable and nurses would routinely get their patients and colleagues to write ditties or poems in them. Many also included illustrations or cartoons drawn by those same patients and colleagues, or by RAMC orderlies and stretcher-bearers. The wartime autograph book became a valuable way of recording the sentiments of soldiers and nurses.

Illustration in a nurse's autograph book, drawn by an injured private of the RAMC who was recovering at number 59 General Hospital, St Omer, 1917. *(Courtesy of Smith Collection)*

Men sometimes found pleasure, solace and sanity in the love of, or the lust for, a woman although for the most part, mothers, wives and sisters were the mainstay of men's cherished beliefs in purity, goodness, innocence and vulnerability. One young soldier from the Royal Irish Fusiliers wrote a very telling letter.

Just a few lines in answer to your very kind and welcomed letter. I am glad to learn that you are in good health. We have advanced a bit further and are a bit excited, for we are thinking now it's us who will attack and not them. Well for my part I do not care for I have nothing to lose but my life, and I am losing it for my mother at home, but I can assure you I will put down 3 or 4 of my enemy before I go. I have no friends only my mother and 3 brothers who are out here in France; they are all alive yet two of them are out from the start and are here yet. Would you be good enough to send me a shaving kit as I have lost all my razors and soap? You have acted as a sister to me and do not trouble yourself anymore. We all think before another month there will be few of us left to trouble anyone.

According to Philip Gibbs, emotional comfort came in many forms.

Down side streets here and there were houses where women catered for the hunger of men exiled year after year from their own home life and decent womanhood. They gave the base counterfeit of love in return for a few francs, and there were long lines of English, Irish and Scottish soldiers, who waited their turn to get that vile imitation of life's romance from women who were bought and paid for.

Prostitution cost the War Office and the forces a 'wastage' per man of approximately 28.6 days hospitalisation for gonorrhoea, 37.6 days for syphilis and 31.3 days for other sexually transmitted diseases. From August 1914 to the Armistice, 153,531 British and Dominion troops were admitted to hospital in France with venereal disease. According to one provost-marshal, three women at a Calais brothel serviced a battalion of men for three weeks after which they retired on their earnings 'pale but proud'.

While sexual gratification was obtained with prostitutes, men wanted love, tenderness and warmth; some believed they had found it in their nurse. It was not uncommon for soldiers to fall in love with, or lust after their nurses. Ivor Gurney, the poet and composer, fell in love with Nurse Annie Drummond when he was invalided to Bangour War Hospital, just outside Edinburgh. The relationship lasted no more than a year. Second Lieutenant Mellersh was wounded at the Somme and sent back to Britain; while recovering in hospital he fell in love with one of his nurses. 'I was in love with a beautiful nurse, a VAD with violet blue eyes, and the dark hair of an Irish girl which she was.' After a period of rehabilitation and recuperation, Mellersh was sent back to France and his relationship with the nurse petered out.

One year later, Second Lieutenant Mellesh was wounded again and, while recovering, fell in love with a nursing sister. 'She was appreciably older than myself, had a large nose, a slow but sweet smile, and an utterly devastating way with her.' It was love from afar and when he was fit to return to active service he 'bought Sister a box of her favourite Russian cigarettes and left it surreptitiously in her private room for her to discover when I had gone and so to remember me'. Some flirtations and relationships ended in marriage.

According to Army Returns, between 1914 and the end of the hostilities, hundreds of marriages outside the United Kingdom were solemnised by Army Chaplains, quite a few between men and nurses on active service.

On the Home Front, men sent back for treatment or convalescence to hospitals in Britain and Ireland found love with women who nursed them. If there was illicit sex between nurses and patients it was seldom discussed or documented, although one poem entitled 'The Night Sister' hinted at what went on for some.

> The ward sister on in the night time,
> Gets pity for missing the sunshine.
> But take it from me,
> It's a jolly old spree.
> 'Thumbs up Boys' says Tommy at light time.

Throughout the war, some artwork depicted the wounded lying in the arms of adoring nurses. Compassion and beauty, masculinity and bravery – it was a heady, potent sensual mixture, contrived by the propagandists for public consumption. Not all men, however, saw nurses as compassionate, beautiful, ministering angels. Some believed nurses were 'sadists'; others claimed the motive to nurse was driven by a 'libidinous streak'. Philip Gibbs, having met many nurses at Casualty Clearing Stations and hospitals, believed them to be:

> ... taking all risks recklessly, playing a man's part with feminine pluck, glad of this liberty, far from the conventions of civilized code, yet giving no hint of scandal to sharp eared gossip.'

There was gossip and, in one case, it led to a scandal. What became known as The Deolali Affair saw five sisters from the Australian Nursing Services accused of immoral behaviour. The sisters were accused of mixing with officers in the evening: one married sister was accused of having a relationship with a sergeant; another was supposed to have had sexual intercourse with a cleaner on the floor of the hospital. The charges were nonsense and an inquiry completely exonerated the nurses of any 'wrongdoing', but the fiasco did highlight the military's concern about relationships between women and men on active service.

Following the conviction of a twenty-one year old VAD for permitting a maisonette at Connaught Street, Hyde Park 'to be used for improper uses', the *British Journal of Nursing* reminded the readership that:

> We have always condemned the practice of the authorities sending young untrained girls to work in military hospitals abroad ... We hope that the

War Office will make it impossible for girls of twenty-one and under to be subjected to the temptations to which this young lady succumbed.

The *British Journal of Nursing* clearly was not in possession of all the facts. The young lady in question had been on active service, but the offence took place in London. Furthermore, in evidence, the young woman claimed that, 'the officers visiting the maisonette were friends' whose acquaintance she had made while working as a VAD nurse in Egypt and elsewhere. It would appear, however, that her version of the story failed to impress both the magistrate and the *British Journal of Nursing*. The young woman was given the option of a £20 fine or six weeks in prison – in addition she was ordered to pay costs.

Companionship, female and male, was important for sustaining morale and a sense of normality and occasional relaxing or breaking of the rules helped nurses cope with the demands of the war, but fraternising with officers and enlisted men was forbidden. Sister Alice Bickmore worked on the hospital trains confirmed that:

> Sisters are not allowed 'out' singly except at the base towns. The rules regulating the social life of sisters are very severe and social intercourse with the medical officers is prohibited. It is, therefore, especially essential that the sisters should have resources in themselves and be on friendly terms.

If rules were made to be broken, then, some nurses did exactly that. Sister Luard had no intention of letting army directives interfere with her need to enjoy herself and have a degree of normality in her demanding and emotionally trying life.

> Went for a walk in the town after tea, and after dinner the OC, Sister B and one of the civil surgeons and the French major and I went to the cinema. It was excellent, or we thought it so, after the months of train and nothing else.

On another occasion, New Year's Eve, she:

> ... went with the major and a French major into Rouen, trotted around sight-seeing. This evening the French staff decorated the restaurant with Chinese lanterns, and we had a festive New Year's dinner, with chicken and Xmas pudding on fire, and Sauterne, Champagne and crackers. The putting on of caps amused every one infiniment.

After an afternoon's celebrations on a newly launched hospital ship, Sister Clarke decided to disappear.

After tea Captain Grieve carried me off to his cabin, with Doctor Isles acting as chaperon, to have cigarettes, leaving the others to amuse themselves. I wonder what the Padre thought! He was sent as watchdog, I'm sure he didn't see anything, as we managed to give him the slip.

Denied the warmth and closeness of relationships, soldiers and nurses found the innocence and vulnerability of animals provided comfort and an antidote to the brutalising effect of war. Doctor John McCrae, who witnessed the first gas attack at Langemarck, and who wrote 'In Flanders Fields', one of the most memorable poems of the war, was concerned about the welfare of animals as well as that of his patients. Two days after the initial gas attack at Langemarck, urgent supplies were being brought up near the location of his advanced dressing station.

The ammunition had to be brought down the roads at the gallop ... the good old horses would swing around at the gallop, pull up in an instant, and stand puffing and blowing, but with their heads up, as if to say, 'Wasn't that well done?' It makes you want to kiss their dear old noses, and assure them of a peaceful pasture once more.' Later in the day he reported, 'Our telephone wagon team hit by a shell; two horses killed, another wounded. I did what I could for the wounded one.' A few days later he was 'adopted' by a frightened dog. 'A big Oxford-grey dog, with beautiful brown eyes, came to us in a panic. He ran to me, and pressed his head hard against my leg. So I got him a safe place and he sticks by us. We call him Fleabag, for he looks like it.

Second Lieutenant John Lucy, 2nd Battalion Royal Irish Rifles, observed that the batman of a fellow officer seemed unduly quiet. He discovered the man was upset by the death of two horses.

The batman was also the transport driver, and his two horses were killed a few nights earlier when the ration party was shelled on the way up to the line ... hours after the shelling he was found draped in the retrieved harness, and weeping bitterly.

Other wagons carried on through the shell-fire but the batman would not leave his dead horses.

Animals were regularly given to or acquired by regiments as mascots. The 4th Northumberland Fusiliers, before they departed for France, were presented with a small terrier called 'Sammy'. He went with the regiment in April 1915 and stayed with his battalion throughout their 1915–1916 trench tours where he suffered from gassing and wounding. Sammy was still with his regiment during the advance on the Somme but, sadly lost his life along with hundreds of his regimental comrades.

According to one army captain, his company acquired a stray Aberdeen terrier which they found in a village. The men named the dog 'Jock' and he stayed with the company for months before he disappeared. The men searched for days but without success and their company was ordered to move on, leaving the little dog somewhere behind them. Weeks later and eighty miles from where they had last seen 'Jock', he turned up. According to the captain, 'Great was our joy. The mystery of how he got there was never solved.' This little dog was lucky as 'Jock' went back to Britain with the men where he lived to a ripe old age.

Nurses too adopted stray dogs and cats which were kept at their billets and Base Hospitals and canaries were on hospital trains to help the morale of patients and nurses. Some hospital trains adopted cats as their mascots and they too happily travelled back and forth with the sick and wounded.

By 1917, Sister Peterkin had transferred from hospitals to the casualty transport barges. She recalled that her barge had acquired an additional member.

> We've got a young magpie on board now. One of the men found it under a tree; it had evidently fallen down and couldn't get up again. They have made a fine big cage for him, out of packing cases and a bit of wire netting. He spends most of his time wandering about the boat and is getting quite tame.

Later she reported:

> Our young magpie is very tame now. It belongs to the Royal Engineers Sergeant, the skipper of the boat, and follows him all over the place. It's a funny wee beast and very knowing. He doesn't like aeroplanes, and whenever one passes over he hops into his box and hides in the corner. He sleeps with the sergeant and wakens him early in the morning by pulling his ear or his hair. In the early days, he twice fell overboard, and had to be fished out the water in a bucket, but now he is more cautious!

For those who smoked, tobacco gave daily relief and comfort. The men were allowed 2 ounces per week, although if they could obtain more, they did. Families regularly sent 'smokes' or 'gaspers' to their loved ones and they were invariably shared with comrades. The tobacco industry did very well out of the men's frustrations, anxieties, fears, and boredom. Between 1910 and 1919, cigarette production increased by 633% from 10 billion per year to 70 billion per year. The YMCA had opposed the use of tobacco, but the circumstances of war made it inevitable that they, too, supplied the troops with cigarettes as a form of comfort and relief.

In 1916, the government believed soldiers in training were using cocaine and it was also pointed out by the Commissioner of Police for London that a number of men had been charged with 'selling, or aiding and abetting the sale of cocaine to His Majesty's Forces'. According to the prosecution counsel, the drug was sold in small pill-boxes, and taken in the form of snuff. In Edwardian Britain, cocaine and opium had become the recreational drugs of choice with the upper classes. Chloroform or 'chlorers' as it was known, and narcotics were readily available if you were 'connected' with the appropriate social class. Cocaine was listed in Part I of the Poisons Schedule and could only be sold by qualified pharmacists to people who were known to them. The government believed the cocaine problem within His Majesty's Forces was big enough to warrant a restriction on its sale.

Alcohol, much to the annoyance of Sir Victor Horsley who tried to have it banned from the services, was being distributed at one-third of a pint of rum per man per week on active service. This was the official rum ration, introduced in the winter of 1914. The rum was distributed in one-gallon earthenware jugs, one jug for sixty-four men, a level of distribution hardly likely to produce an army of alcoholics.

When behind the line, men could obtain alcohol from estaminets, which generally sold cheap wine and weak beer. One medical officer noted that:

> Champagne containing raw spirit at 10 francs a bottle, and wine fortified with illicit rum, are causing a lot of drunkenness. Half a mile from the billet the senior stretcher-bearer lay for hours, quite incapable.

General Percy Crozier tried to have spirits banned from the army in France and was impressed that the French had taken steps to ban spirits for the French troops.

An off-duty nurse with adopted dogs at the nurses' billets, number 11 Stationary Hospital, Rouen.
*(Courtesy of Smith Collection)*

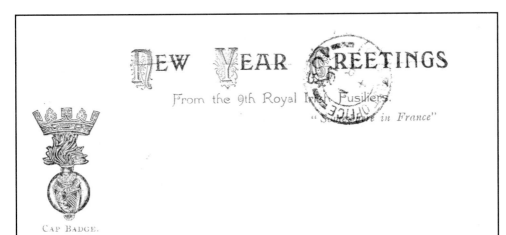

**Regimental Post Card - sent by a soldier of the Royal Irish Fusiliers to Mr W. Ross of Lurgan. The card reads: 'Dear Sir, I received the cigarettes alright and thanking you very much for same'.** *(Courtesy of Doherty Collection)*

With us the drinking of spirits was made easy. Canteens and clubs behind the lines and at bases were stocked with alcohol. Profiteers made money out of it at the expense of the youth of the nation … I have heard it said that the British Empire was consolidated with the aid of 'baccy' [tobacco], beer and the Bible, plus the gallant efforts of the British soldier. I have no doubt about the latter; but the record of beer and the Bible in the war leaves me stone cold.

The exchange of letters and postcards from home was probably the greatest comfort of all and by 1917 the Army on the Western Front was sending home 8,150,000 letters every week. The censoring of mail, however, meant that people back home did not know where their loved ones were and what they were doing. In November 1916 the *Censorship Orders and Regulations for Troops in the Field* were introduced, reaffirming the need for the good censorship practice that had been introduced at the beginning of the war. The key points for reinforcement were that no information on troop movements was to be given; discussing military issues while on leave was to be avoided; no reference was to be made to the effects of hostile fire on the troops; and the reporting of the physical and morale effects of fighting was forbidden.

Sister Clarke highlighted the problem. 'Tonight I will write home, as I haven't had time all week; of course one couldn't tell them any news.' For some, the inability to communicate freely with family and friends led to feelings of isolation and finding ways of getting information back to families became a priority. A letter, sent to the family of a nurse from a soldier on leave, explained the problem that many nurses faced.

> Sister has asked me as I was coming home on leave, to let you know her whereabouts, as she is debarred from telling you herself, owing to the censor. She is at Number Eight British Red Cross Hospital, which is run by the London Corn Exchange. This hospital is situated on the coast, by Le Touquet. As the censorship at this hospital is exceptionally strict, not only as regards information but especially as regards criticism of the hospital and its officers, you will understand why probably she seldom refers to the hospital in letters.

Sister Peterkin found ways of getting information back home.

> Large number of men have been sent off today by hospital ship for home, more will go tomorrow. Everyone taking advantage of a chance to get letters home!

Nurses, however, were not immune to receiving letters informing them of the death of a family member or friend on active service. There was also always the possibility they could meet a serving family member or friend if they were brought in sick or wounded to Casualty Clearing Stations or Base Hospitals.

Sister Luard's brother was killed in the 1915 Gallipoli campaign. The poet, Captain Julian Grenfell, sustained serious injuries when he was struck by an enemy shell; he was taken to a Base Hospital at Wimereux where his sister, Monica, worked as a VAD nurse and where he died of his wounds at the age of 27. Two months later, Monica lost her other brother on active service. Sister Waldock from the Australian Nursing Service had five brothers at the front and two were killed in action. Staff Nurse Norah Claye had a father and brother serving at the Front and her brother was killed in 1917. Millicent Peterkin recalled how one of her colleagues received notification of a family member being injured.

Sister O'Conner got a wire from her people, saying that her brother had been wounded, and asking her to go to him if possible. She spent a very anxious evening and night, as she did not know where he was. Matron started phoning to various hospitals, then the telephone broke down, so no more news to be got through. Yesterday forenoon she got word that he was in No 11 General at Boulogne, wounded in the head, and progressing favourably. The necessary passports, etc., were obtained, and O'Conner left here at nine o'clock last night, on four days leave.

Twenty four hours later, Sister Peterkin recorded, 'O'Conner came back this evening, having just missed her brother, who had gone to England.'

Sisters in Casualty Clearing Stations or hospitals had the sad but essential job of writing to families to explain the wounding, illness or death of their loved ones. In some instances, the family could not be traced.

Dear Miss ——
I am writing to you as your address was found in the pocket of Rifleman … who was brought here yesterday most grievously wounded and although everything possible was done for him he passed away a few hours later. He was wounded in the head and was quite unconscious so we could get no clue to any relationships. If you are just a friend will you be kind enough to send this letter to his people. You will like to know he was spared pain, in a comfortable bed in a warm room, and had all that was necessary for his comfort. He did not speak at all so could leave no messages. He is buried in the cemetery near here and is marked by a cross and is nicely kept. I may not give the name of the place but the authorities at the War Office will give it to you if you wish. His belongings will be sent to his next-of-kin later.
With sympathy for his people in their loss.
Believe me
Yours faithfully,
A. M. Raine
Sister in Charge

This Rifleman belonged to the Monmouthshire Regiment, 1st Battalion. He was 21 years of age when he died on 2 May 1917 at Number 6 Casualty Clearing Station and was buried alongside 1,094 of his comrades. He left a mother to mourn him.

For the nurses on active service, there were consistent causes of distress, annoyance and irritation. They were confronted by interminable bureaucracy, moving from hospital to hospital with the attendant problems of breaking established relationships, frequently having little food and sleep, being either too hot or cold, inadequate billeting, isolation from family and friends, censorship of mail, and concern and worry about the safety of family members or friends who were on active service. There is no doubt that life and work were physically and emotionally taxing for nurses but for the most part, this was met with a mixture of irritation and good grace, balanced by camaraderie and humour.

In an open letter to her colleagues, printed in the *The Nursing Times*, a nurse described the attributes needed for working at the Western Front, and advised that any nurses planning to volunteer for service should be aware of the qualities needed to sustain them through the harshness of the working and living conditions.

I should say that endurance and tact are the most important qualities for a war nurse to possess. Anyone intending to volunteer for active service should spend a 'thought hour' of self-examination and see if she can answer such questions as these. Are you ready to give up many of the personal comforts which, upon the present time, you may have looked upon as mere necessities, but which will become impossible luxuries? Are you prepared to face damp and cold so intense and persistent that some days you will seriously doubt if undressing will be possible? And when this difficulty has been overcome and you have tucked yourself under as many covers as you can stand, you begin to wonder if you will ever be able to get up and dress when the morning comes! Your hot water bag becomes cold in a very short time, your tent walls and bed covers are soon covered with frost, and you are lucky if your discomfort is not made worse by chilblains which are 'punishing' you dreadfully for having covered them up and tried to make them warm. The cold may be so intense that your hands are blue and numb, but the work has to be done and sometimes you will have to check tears of real suffering and do your duty. Your laundry will be a great problem, for weeks at a time you may not be able to have any done. It will be most necessary for you to leave all your 'food fads' at home and your well-being will depend upon your readiness to eat what is put before you. Our personal independence must be placed under control. Many can put up with the discomforts for a time, but are you prepared to 'stick it out'? That is the question you must answer. Endurance means all this as well as the power to work under the double physical and mental strain that accompanies war nursing. Tact, which I consider second only to endurance, will help you over many a rough road. In dealing with the medical profession it will be news to no one if I say that you will need much tact. Good health is essential. You must remember that your hands are going to be quite full enough without having to worry about yourself and no one else will have time to do so. A bright disposition should accompany the above qualifications, and it is a great asset under the depressing conditions. Patience!!!! Bring it all with you and if you have not much of it, beg, borrow or steal some. If you feel that you can answer the call and see it through to the best of your ability, and in spite of all the hardships, you will find it the most satisfying work you have ever done and you will never regret having undertaken it.

For some men unable to find solace or spiritual comfort for their fears and anxieties, suicide or a self-inflicted wound was their only way out of the war. By 1917, Catherine Black was in charge of 100 men with self-inflicted wounds and claimed:

> It is hard to nurse a man who is wounded or very ill, and remember all the time that he is a prisoner awaiting court-martial. I used to constantly forget it, a fact which often drew down on my head an official rebuke.

On one occasion, Sister Black was reprimanded for giving her patients eggs for tea and the CO reminded her that she 'must remember that they are prisoners and cannot expect any privileges.' She was aware that the men who deliberately injured themselves to avoid further war service were viewed by the High Command as cowards and they had to be punished.

> They were mere boys of fifteen or sixteen, who had joined up by putting down their age as twenty-one. It had been fine in the first glow of patriotism … but they became more and more afraid, until at last they had only been frightened children looking for the quickest way out.

Over the coming months, it was not only child soldiers who were looking for a way out. Every kind of belief, superstition and relationship would be called upon to help the men of the British and Dominion forces fight through the grotesque horror that was Passchendaele, where men believed they were being murdered by a high command which cared more about winning the war than the human cost being paid. A soldier of the Queen's Own Cameron Highlanders was unable to contain his thoughts on the slaughter when General Gough inspected what was left of the soldier's battalion. The General remained mounted on the back of his horse as he addressed the men, saying, 'I deplore your losses. I am sure you will all want to avenge their deaths so I am making you up with a large draft so that you can return and avenge your comrades.' 'You're a bloody butcher,' the soldier shouted.

The death rate from wounding and disease was rising in the nursing ranks. On 3 March 1917, the *Asturias* was torpedoed by a U boat. One nursing sister was among 35 lost. This was followed on 10 April by the sinking of the Hospital Ship *Salta,* where 52 lives were lost, 8 of them nurses: 1 matron, 3 sisters and 4 staff-nurses. Between July and October, air raids on several Casualty Clearing Stations took the lives of 3 nurses and wounded several more. Some of the nurses injured in the raids were sent back home with broken legs, broken ribs, disfiguring wounds and neurasthenia. On the last day of the year, the *Osmanieh* was hit by a mine; 200 lives were lost and these included 8 nurses: 3 sisters, 1 staff nurse, 3 VAD nurses and 1 probationer. By the end of 1917, between active service, sickness, injury and drowning, a total of 54 nurses had lost their lives.

The number of men who spent the last Christmas of the war in hospitals in France was 100,322 – almost double the numbers in 1916. The sick and wounded admitted to hospitals for treatment during 1917 came to 1,606,960.

The 1917 campaigns at Arras, Messines, Passchendaele and Cambrai had cost the British and Dominion forces dearly, but the war was not yet over. They had paid an intolerable blood tax and would be asked to pay it again. In the coming year, soldiers and nurses would continue to be sustained by spirituality, inspiration and esprit de corps in their efforts to achieve victory.

**VAD and FANY ambulance drivers, with mascots.** *(Courtesy of Smith Collection)*

Chapter VIII

## *'When this Bloody War Is Over'*

# Fortitude, Finale and Legacy 1918

At the end of 1917 *The Times* stopped publishing complete casualty lists. On a day-by-day basis throughout the war, the paper had published endless lists of the Killed in Action, Died of Wounds, Wounded, Wounded – Shell Shock, Missing, and Prisoner in Enemy Hands. There could be as many as 5,000 names printed and the number seldom fell below 1,000 names per day. Such was the daily reminder of the loss of family, friends and colleagues, that Nancy Astor claimed, 'We do not look at the casualty lists any more. There was nothing to look for. All of our friends had gone.' By 1918, traumatic losses had brought with them a search for meaning, and – a thriving business opportunity. Alleged 'psychic interventions' with dead soldiers, which began in earnest in 1915, was now well established. In the absence of a body to grieve over, and denied the ritual of burial, thousands of bereaved families were attempting to make contact with their dead loved ones. There were, of course, any number of charlatans prepared to play on the raw emotions of the bereaved. The call on mediums and psychic healers had become so prevalent that, according to the *Daily Mail*, at least three hundred 'seers' had come to the attention of the authorities in the West End of London: men and women who were attempting to make their fortune out of the misfortunes of war. In response to these parasitic practices the Witchcraft Act (1732) and Vagrancy Act (1824) were used to bring about prosecutions.

Within the Forces, the loss of life affected every social class. Herbert Asquith, who had been Prime Minister until late 1916, lost his son, Raymond, in September of that year while leading an attempt to take the notorious Quadrilateral on the Somme. Andrew Bonar Law, Chancellor of the Exchequer, lost two sons; Arthur Henderson, Leader of the Labour Party, lost his son, Sir Harry Lauder received a telegram from the Home Office on New Year's Day informing him of the death of his only son, and Sir Arthur Conan Doyle lost his son. Conan Doyle was to become a devotee of spiritualism and did much to promote understanding of it, publishing in 1918, *The New*

*Revelation,* his study on psychic and spiritual phenomenon.

Men, women, and boys were lost to the dirty business of a war which had become ethically and morally more questionable. Grieving parents were haunted by having to confront the death of their child or children. It was not uncommon to have several sons serving at the front, and to be notified by the War Office that none of them would be returning home. In their desperation to accept, or sometimes deny, their loved ones' deaths, many turned, not to the established cultural and social expressions of mourning, but to the practice of spiritualism. Just as the serving men and women on the Western Front had found various ways to accommodate the intensity or negativity of their feelings, on the Home Front, grieving and distraught families, lovers, and friends turned to a variety of beliefs and rituals.

As an outward demonstration of collective grief, street shrines became popular in cities, towns and villages. They were constructed by the local community, and varied in size, craftsmanship and content. Some were wooden boards or thick wooden or metal plaques, which had the names of the war dead inscribed, painted or carved onto them. Many shrines were built into buildings with architectural recesses where wooden shelves or altars could be constructed. They were generally draped in flags and adorned with flowers; some communities had religious emblems or statues as the focal point. They were erected as a labour of love and they were maintained by communal grief. In addition to these informal commemorations and dedications, there were regular 'In Remembrance of the Dead' services, which were usually conducted 'in praise of gallant and noble sacrifice'. These were seen by some cynics as a means of controlling the outpouring of grief.

In London, on 10 April 1918, a memorial service was held in St Paul's Cathedral for 'all the nurses who have fallen during the war.' Queen Alexandra, Princess Victoria and other members of the Royal family attended the service. The Archdeacon of London, V. E. Holmes, concluded in his eulogy that 'you have had your chance and you have taken it – women who will be remembered with the soldiers in a never-to-be-forgotten page of history'. He reminded the matrons, sisters and nurses present that they were entrusted with 'great work' and, because of that work, were gathered to worship in memory of their dead colleagues. He also commented that the future of nursing was very dependent on the assembled nurses and that the sacrifices made by the nurses who went off to war should never be forgotten. If the Archdeacon was implying that their sacrifices were over, his sentiments were premature, for nurses and everyone else, the war was not yet over. After four years of murderous conflict both sides were physically and psychologically exhausted, thousands were traumatised, but no one knew how to stop the killing.

The spring of 1918 saw the Germans launch a death or glory offensive in a bid to break the allied defences. Every type of weapon was marshalled for the destruction of the Allied Forces in the belief that this was to be the final push to secure their victory. On 21 March, on a line between Arras and La Fère, 74 German divisions massed for an attack on the British 3rd and 5th Armies. Within a four-hour period on the first day of the offensive, the Germans fired 1,000,000 shells. Overwhelmed, the British began a retreat that ended ten days later at Amiens.

Sister Black, who latterly had been working in Casualty Clearing Stations, claimed that her most vivid recollections of all her wartime experiences were:

> ... that nightmare retreat in the spring of 1918 and its aftermath of air-raid terrors ... For twenty four hours we sat or huddled on the floor of our lorry following a hurried flight from Sailly Lorette, living a sort of confused nightmare. Our orders were to drive to Amiens and await instruction there.

Arriving in Amiens, Sister Black witnessed scenes of confusion and chaos.

> The last remnants of the civilian population were fleeing from the German advance ... and as fast as one set of inhabitants poured out of the town another was pouring in. Troops, weary and mud stained from the trenches, roamed through the streets in a vain search for billets ... Hundreds of wounded men evacuated from every casualty clearing station along the line lay on stretchers just where the ambulance men had put them ... Every hospital in Amiens was already filled to overflowing. Surgeons and nurses who had got detached from their units and lost all their equipment were going around doing what they could with dressings and drugs taken from chemists' shops.

Finding herself detached from her own unit, Sister Black and her colleague, Sister Duggan, went in search of the people they knew.

> Little Sister Duggan and I set off together and, both being Irish and fatalists chose the road straight ahead of us ... We tramped for an hour or more but without success ... we passed a number of surgeons and nurses, but none could help us. They were all too intent on finding their own units. Suddenly, we heard a voice crying in the rich brogue of Donegal, 'Mother of God let them get me a drop of water.' The cry had come from a building on our right ... we pushed the gate open and went in ... We found ourselves in the courtyard of an orphanage, but instead of French children, there were rows of British wounded lying on stretchers. They

had been brought in, 200 or more of them, from an evacuated CCS, and left there temporarily in the confusion of the retreat without anyone to attend to them ... Sister Duggan and I exchanged one horrified glance of comprehension and in that moment forgot about finding our unit. We rolled up our sleeves and set to.

In an inaccurate piece of reporting which angered and demoralised nurses, *The Times* indicated that, in the retreat, the order 'nurses first', not patients, had been given, a procedure the *British Journal of Nursing* contended was 'contrary to all precedent where British Nurses are concerned.' Much to the delight if not relief, of serving nurses, Philip Gibbs described the retreat and the sisters' roles in it. He was able to reassure nurses and the public that he had witnessed sisters being put on any vehicle going back from the line once the wounded had been dispatched to safety.

They were squeezed between drivers and men on motor lorries, sitting amongst our Tommies on motor lorries, one at least on a gun limber, and others perched on the top of forage, still merry and bright in spite of the tragedy about them, because that is their training and their faith.

In the course of the retreat, the Germans bombed an ambulance convoy, killing one sister, two ambulance drivers and patients; several other nurses sustained injuries. The *British Journal of Nursing* had previously referred to the bombing of hospitals and ambulances as the 'barbarous war on the wounded' and that 'unimpeachable testimony of eye-witnesses at the front' proved that the bombing of hospitals by the Germans was 'done deliberately, that helpless sick and wounded are thus murdered in cold blood, and doctors, nurses or other humane people liable to share their fate.' Over the next five months, this pattern of chaos and danger would seriously interrupt the work of nurses and end many of their lives.

The New Year had got off to a bad start for medical and nursing services. On 4 January, a U boat sank the Hospital Ship *Rewa,* off the Bristol Channel with the loss of 4 lives. After drifting in their lifeboats for two hours, patients, nurses and doctors were picked up and taken to the nearest port before being transferred to local hospitals. In February, on her outward journey, the *Glenart Castle* was sunk in the Bristol Channel with the loss of 162 lives including 8 nurses, 7 RAMC medical officers and 47 medical orderlies. The Matron of the *Glenart*, Miss Kate Beaufoy, a South African War veteran, had worked on several hospital ships since the beginning of the war and travelled 60,000 miles caring for 30,000 patients. Tragically for Miss Beaufoy and the patients, nurses and doctors, this was the seventh British hospital ship to be sunk within a year. On 26 June, HMHS *Llandovery Castle* was sunk by a U-boat 120 miles from the Irish coast with the loss of 146 lives including 14 sisters. Two more nursing sisters died between August and October when the *China* and *Leinster* were attacked by U boats.

Between March and June, 8 nursing sisters died in enemy air raids on Casualty Clearing Stations and Base Hospitals and between 15 May and 1 June, Base Hospitals on the north coast of France were bombed seven times killing 248 and wounding 593. Included were 5 sisters killed and 11 injured. A sister claimed 89 nurses who had been shelled out of Casualty Clearing Stations arrived at her Base Hospital.

They had a most awful experience. One English sister was killed instantaneously. The shell burst just outside the tent – a piece of shrapnel shot through her tent piercing the subclavien artery – she died ten minutes later. Three orderlies were also killed and several wounded. At the Canadian Casualty Clearing Station a sister lost her right eye. Goodness knows what is going to happen. It was awful seeing these sisters when they arrived just collapsing on the floor – some fast asleep with their heads resting on their kit-bags just like the boys. Several of the sisters have had to be evacuated because of shell shock.

The tragic loss of life from bombing raids on Casualty Clearing Stations was summed up in a poignant obituary:

In ever loving memory of Lieutenant —— of the Middlesex Regiment (the 'Die Hards'), the darling son of —— who was foully bombed to death the 30th of May during an air raid on one of the hospitals in France, where he was lying utterly helpless after an operation (he was taken there on the 27th of May), aged nearly 21.

It is not surprising that, in 1918, higher instances of debility, nervous debility, neurasthenia and conditions such as 'Exhaustion Psychosis' were diagnosed in nurses. Despite coping with the hardship of their physical surroundings, some nurses could no longer endure the sight of so much human suffering in some of the men they nursed. One sister nursing gassing victims was under considerable emotional strain:

I have had a particularly hard ten days, and have been on duty from a quarter past seven to nine at night. We have had a very bad convoy in, terribly burnt, and with their lungs in a dreadful state and, in spite of all we could do, a great number died in terrible agony ... I have seen things here that I shall never be able to forget ... I have the small wards for the very bad cases, and the isolation-room for the dying, and since I have been here, particularly the last fortnight, I have felt as though I was living through a hideous nightmare, with visions of choking men, with blackened, burnt faces being held down by orderlies and attached to their beds to prevent them throwing themselves out of the window in their last struggles for breath.

Another sister believed that, in her four years of war nursing, caring for the victims of gassing was 'the most fatiguing; there is an indescribable feeling of tiredness, lassitude and depression and it is very sad, very sad, so many dying, and the death so agonising.'

In spite of everything they witnessed, nurses were not, in the main, debilitated by psychological problems. This point was made about women generally in a report by Dr George Robertson, Physician-Superintendent, of the Royal Edinburgh Mental Hospital:

> The amount of insanity amongst women has not increased, but has tended to decrease. Although there have been many cases of mental breakdown among women from excitement from overwork and exhaustion, and from worry and anxiety, on the whole the strain and conditions produced by the war have not resulted in an increased amount of insanity.

Although there were cases of nurses breaking down under the strain of war, it was the conditions in which they lived and worked that affected them most. Their physical ill health was caused by tuberculosis, bronchitis, pneumonia, heart disease, arthritis and injury which, since 1914, had been the most common causes of long term sickness and retirement from the military nursing service.

The tenacity and dedication of some nurses is explified in a report in the *Liverpool Daily Post* of Sister E. J. French of the QAIMNS, a native of Liverpool attached to the BEF who had crossed to France in a cattle boat in August 1914. In her time with the army she had travelled in cattle trucks, slept on brick floors and under canvas for months, was shelled, gassed and, finally, contracted trench-fever. From her hospital bed at No 2 General Hospital, Le Havre, where she lay dangerously ill, she wrote that she was not too well but was going to 'stick it out, as I came out with the 'Old Contemptibles', I should like to go home with them.'

It was not only in the worsening conditions of the Front or at sea that nurses were at risk. In Sister French's native Liverpool, an inquest was held into the circumstances surrounding the death of forty-year old Nurse McShane. According to the court report:

> Mr. William Henry Taylor, officer in charge of Belmont Road Military Auxiliary Hospital, Liverpool, said the hospital contained black and

white patients, the former being British West Indians. The coloured men had been over-staying the time allowed them out of hospital.

In consequence the military police guard was redoubled and the names and numbers of the men were taken. Wednesday, last week, a West Indian sergeant, named Demetrius, attempted to leave the hospital. He was stopped, but immediately drew a razor and slashed wildly with it. He was disarmed and placed in a cell. Ten men, all West Indians then appeared. Two of the number refused to go to their wards, and, being joined by four or five other coloured men, became very abusive. An attempt was made to take them to the cells, and fifty other West Indians joined in the affair, taking possession of the police lodge. Some 400 wounded British soldiers, who were at a concert in the hospital hall, came to the rescue of the military police. There was a struggle, in which crutches and sticks were freely used, and pots and pans were flying about. The police were reinforced and order was restored. Unfortunately, Nurse McShane, while helping another girl, was caught in the rush of men. She was carried off her feet and was knocked down. She suffered from shock, but no severe injuries. Pneumonia developed, and she died four days later. After hearing medical evidence, the inquest returned a verdict of 'Death through misadventure'.

In characteristic style, the *British Journal of Nursing* commented that:

When one reads of the death of a nurse owing to a disturbance in a military hospital, one wonders who is responsible for the discipline of the institution, for evidently it requires twitching up.

In Ireland, a public meeting was held in Dublin at the Royal Dublin Society, its main objective to establish a fund for the benefit of all Irish Certificated Nurses. It was suggested that, as a mark of the country's gratitude, a hostel should be endowed for those who needed it. The Lord Chancellor of Ireland, Sir James Campbell, presided over the meeting, and Sir Arthur Stanley MP, Chairman of the Joint War Committee of the British Red Cross and the Order of St John, was the principal speaker. Sir James said that the meeting was held to determine how best the nation could acknowledge the response that the women of Ireland, particularly nurses, had made to the war effort. Sir Arthur said:

We know what they (women) have done in regard to the supply depots, which supply everything required for the surgical and medical comforts of our wounded soldiers, but the immediate concern is with the efforts made by Irishwomen as trained nurses in the field and hospitals.

It was anticipated that many nurses, having served at the Front, would return to Ireland with nervous exhaustion. A Hostel for their rest and recuperation would be an ideal gift from a thankful nation. Unfortunately, returning Irish soldiers would receive no such consideration. Since the Easter Rising in Dublin, the political climate had changed and there was now, in the south of Ireland, open hostility to Irishmen serving in the British Army.

While the Irish authorities debated how the women of Ireland could best be acknowledged for their war work, the plight of long-term, sick and disabled British and Irish nurses generally was not capturing adequate attention from the Government, the nursing press or the nursing leadership. It did, however, attract the interest of the national press. In response to letters published in *The Times* alleging neglect of the physical and psychological health of nurses on active service, *The Nursing Times* ran a series of articles entitled 'The Care of War Nurses'. It concluded that, on a recent trip to France, a representative of *The Nursing Times* found 'military nurses absolutely cheerful, happy and loyal'. An editorial, following a fact-finding trip to France, demonstrated even less sympathy:

> It seems strange that this critical time when our men are fighting to the death and our nurses are working night and day should be chosen by some to complain of the conditions of Army Nurses ... It strikes us that those who complain have not grasped the conditions.

The nursing leadership and the editors of their journals also lacked sympathy. Nurses from all branches of the military nursing services and the British Red Cross Society who became ill or sustained injuries directly attributed to their war service, were facing severe financial hardship. The Editorial reminded its readership that:

> A nurse might work five years for a hospital or a co-operation; if she was unlucky enough to break down, she could not expect from these institutions a life pension; why, then, if she goes in for war work and breaks down after a year or two, should she expect to be permanently provided for? We are putting the position very harshly because we are writing from the practical business point of view, but as a matter of fact the real position is not as hard as that.

The case of a sister who had been injured in a bombing raid on a Casualty Clearing Station in France in 1917 illustrates the hardships which could confront nurses who became ill or suffered injuries. According to the medical reports:

> The whole of the calf of one leg was blown off, skin, muscle, nerves and vessels all gone, and the fibula fractured and she was now walking with a limp.

Her injuries had been classified by a medical board as 'permanent'. After corrective surgery to her great toe which became contracted as a consequence of her injury, causing her considerable pain when walking, the medical board re-assessment concluded that, 'the injury impairs the activity of Sister ... but does not debar her from light work.' The sister was awarded a 40% disability pension for eight months at £40 per year. On an appeal to the Government's War Pensions Department, it was claimed by her medical practitioner and petitioner that:

> She cannot go out of the house alone and it would be very kind of you if you let her know what steps she ought to take in order to have the decision of the Pensions Board revised. I am not at all surprised to hear that she is so helpless for quite apart from any damage to deeper structures, the loss of such a large area of skin on a lower limb is certain to result in so delicate a scar that any attempt to get about would be likely to make the scar tissue break down.

The Queen Alexandra Fund for War Nurses, established in 1915 to assist nurses who were not in the regular military nursing services, but had volunteered through the British Red Cross for war work, had, according to *The Nursing Times,* assisted 386 cases and spent £22,875 in providing 'hospitality and giving grants for convalescence ... All the nurses have been able to return to work and there has been only one death from tuberculosis.' The journal was clearly unaware of a number of deaths between 1914 and 1918 of nurses who served under the auspices of the Red Cross. The Editorial went on to state that, 'for the regular services there are good pensions, and the cases of those who have joined since the war are considered by a Medical Board and helped in every possible way.'

This was not the case for a sister who had served in the QAIMNS and was injured in a bombing raid on No 61 Casualty Clearing Station in August 1917. Having received shrapnel and gunshot wounds to her left leg, the proceedings of the medical board considered her to have 'no disability'. Writing to the Matron-in-Chief of the QAIMNS from a nursing home in Edinburgh where she was being cared for, she asked:

> Would you kindly forward me a form and particulars regarding wound gratuity ... Since my return to civil work I find that the wound interferes very much with the free action of my leg and in that way incapacitates me for my normal day's work.

The District Awards Branch granted her a one-off payment of £15.

Nurses applying for war pensions were suffering varying degrees of hardship. One of the most telling cases involved a nursing sister who married a soldier she had been caring for. The soldier was permanently blinded in both eyes and she herself subsequently sustained an eye injury while on active service. It was only after her eye sight deteriorated that she applied to the Ministry of Pensions for a War Pension, but she was refused. She wrote the following to the Pensions Office:

> May I ask you to reconsider the decision of the late Minister of Pensions that I applied too late for a pension for the loss of sight in my right eye from an injury sustained in the war ... I joined up in 1914 and nursed in several places in England also on Hospital ships. I received from the British Government the 1914 Star, the overseas medal and the Victory Medal, and a beautiful certificate in recognition of valuable services rendered in the Great War... I did not ask for a pension until the other eye began to get affected, I am almost totally blind and dependant on my husband's pension who was totally blinded and badly wounded in the war.

Two years after her appeal for reconsideration of a war pension, the nurse was informed that, 'your case has been considered and it has been decided to make you a grant, under special sanction, at the rate of £75 per year.'

The allocation of pensions appears to have been almost arbitrary and it would be difficult to know exactly what criteria were applied for an award to be made. The table opposite gives a few examples of the disabilities for which nurses received pensions and the length of time which applied. First names only have been used so that these women cannot be identified.

The death rate in the nursing services between 1914 and 1918 had gone from 4 in 1914 to 161 in 1918. The bombing of Casualty Clearing Stations and the torpedoing of ships led to an increase in death and injuries and the number of sick also increased significantly. The last year of the war pushed everyone, not least nurses, to the limits of their endurance.

On Saturday the 26 October, two weeks before the Armistice, the *British Journal of Nursing* declared:

> Victory in View – Now that after four years of war, of a magnitude and horror unknown in the history of the world, the victory of the Allies, and the triumph of the right and just are in sight, none rejoice more than trained nurses, who from their intimate association with the wounded in the clearing stations and close behind the firing line, realise most poignantly the splendour of the valour of the allied troops, whether fighting with the enemy, or maimed and wounded enduring the results of the conflict in hospital wards.

The last hundred days of the war finally brought a 'victorious end' for Britain

**A rare photograph of a group of Allied soldiers, taken by Sister Smith at the end of hosilities.**
*(Courtesy of Smith Collection)*

| Nurse | Nature of Disability | Pensionable Years |
|---|---|---|
| Julia | Debility | 1915-1949 |
| Florence | Fractured Femur | 1917-1942 |
| Ernestine | Nephritis | 1916-1968 |
| Clara | Hemiplegia | 1916-1935 |
| Joanna | Confusional Insanity | 1918-1937 |
| Ethel | Malaria | 1919-1928 |
| Elizabeth | Appendicitis (Effects of) | 1919-1931 |
| Violet | Congenital Tabes | 1920-1968 |
| Florence | Varicose Veins/Anaemia | 1919-1925 |
| Lilian | Hysterical Neurasthenia | 1920-1930 |
| Ann | Fractured Femur | 1917-1948 |
| Alice | Disordered Action of the Heart | 1919-1927 |
| Florence | Debility | 1919-1923 |
| Laura | Tuberculosis | 1918-1981 |
| Alicia | Debility/Tuberculosis | 1902-1948 |
| Violet | Asthma/Nephritis | 1918-1938 |
| Margaret | Rheumatism/Hypertension | 1918-1932 |
| Olivia | Malaria | 1918-1920 |

**BUCKINGHAM PALACE.**

*1918.*

The Queen & I wish you God-speed, a safe return to the happiness & joy of home life with an early restoration to health.

A grateful Mother Country thanks you for faithful services.

*George R.I.*

**A letter from the King to the sick and injured. It arrived in an envelope with the words 'A Message to You From the King' printed on the front. The mass-produced 'letter' was received by millions.** *(Courtesy of Doherty Collection)* and her allies following a four-year brutally contested, savagely fought campaign. On the eleventh hour of the eleventh day of the eleventh month, Armistice Day finally arrived. It was fitting that church bells rang out 'Tipperary' at Mons, the site of the first BEF engagement and only captured that morning. It had indeed been a long, long way to victory. On the Western Front in that month alone, there were 107,472 sick and wounded men in hospitals and hospital trains; a further 1,905 were in transit to various treatment and embarkation centres. These included 6,378 prisoners of war. In reality, there were no victors: everyone lost someone or something of themselves.

Perhaps the war could best be summed up by the words of Major Frank Watson who had been mobilised with his Territorial battalion in 1914 and survived the war.

> The War as a whole was a crime and a tragedy ... The men on both sides were sacrificed, as they always have been, to retrieve the errors of the statesmen and the generals. But sharing toil, exhaustion, hardship and danger does not destroy a man's soul. The soldier is not the man who makes war; he is the man who offers his life to end it.

Sister Luard, who saw first hand the consequences of the 'errors of statesmen and generals', survived four years of back and heart-breaking nursing. Her strength of character, sense of humour and humanity enabled her to move between extremes of situations and emotions in an instant without losing her professionalism, equanimity and consideration for men of all backgrounds and ranks. An extract from her 1917 war diary amply illustrates this.

> Thursday, August 2nd, 11.45 p.m.
> The uproar went on all night no one slept much. It made one realise how far up we are to have streams of shells crossing over our heads. The rain continues all night and all day since the Push began on Monday ... The men are brought in with mud over their eyes and mouths, and 126 have died in 3½ days.
> General Sir Hubert Gough, and some of his Staff paid us a long visit this morning ... We stood in the rain and mud with streams trickling off our Brass Hats and Sou'westers down our backs, and he asked how we stuck it all, and I assured him we were all right. The Colonel told him about the shelling and said the Sisters enjoyed it! (Glad he thought so!)
> One boy of 18 said, 'Will you write to Mother? Give her my love. Say I'm all right; she's an invalid. Mind you write her a comfortin' letter.' An oldish man wanted to be lifted up in the bed; when we'd done it, he murmured, 'What would we do without women in the world!' And they don't expect to find women up here.

Yesterday morning Captain ... V.C. and Bar, D.S.O., M.C., R.A.M.C., was brought in badly hit in the tummy and arm and had been going about for two days with a scalp wound till he got hit. Half the Regiment have been to see him; he is loved by everybody. He was quickly X-rayed, operated on, shrapnel found, holes sewn up, salined and put to bed. He is just on the borderland still; better this afternoon and perhaps going to do, but not so well to-night. He tries hard to live; he was going to be married. [Although she did not name him, this was Doctor Noel Chavasse]

Sunday, August 5th, 11.30 p.m.
Captain ... died yesterday; four of us went to his funeral to-day; and a lot of the MOs; two of them wheeled the stretcher and lowered him. His horse was led in front and then the pipers and masses of kilted officers followed. Our Padre with his one arm, Father E. looked like a Prophet towering over everybody and saying it all without book. After the Blessing one Piper came to the graveside (which was a large pit full of dead soldiers sewn up in canvas) and played a lament. Then his Colonel, who particularly loved him, stood and saluted him in his grave. It was fine, but horribly choky.

Sister Black's insight, understanding and empathy created a safe haven in which traumatised soldiers could express their feelings of fear, despair and shame. Where would those men with self-inflicted wounds and shell shock have been without her and women like her? Reflecting on the tragedy of the men she had cared for, she wrote poignantly, 'I sometimes wonder what has become of them; what life has given them in exchange for the youth they lost.' Of the dying men she nursed in Casualty Clearing Stations, she lamented:

You went first to the men who were visibly dying and gave each one an injection of morphia. It was all you could do for them. You had seen death many times in your hospital training, but it had been different then, for He had come for the old or for those weakened by illness. Not this harvest of the young and strong who had been full of life only a few hours before.

Of the three Sisters whose words are quoted throughout this work, Sister Peterkin was the youngest but youthfulness did not deter her determination and dedication. Thankfully, her sense of justice and fair play made her a wonderful advocate for her wartime patients and colleagues. The manner in which she handled a problem she encountered with French railway officials when trying to find seating accommodation on a train en route to her posting at No. 9 General Hospital, perhaps illustrates her scant regard for authority.

We had great difficulty in getting a carriage. There was a whole first-class one at the end of the train, but a French official refused to let us in and got fearfully excited, saying it was for passengers! We said we were passengers, and simply got in, baggage and all, and sat down. We were backed up by the Sergeant Major and all the Sergeants, who were in the next carriage. The Frenchman stormed and raved, and brought more officials, who declared the train would not go till we got out, but we sat still, and finally we started!

The dogged determination and commitment that kept her going through four years of nursing on the Western Front allowed her to deal with some very distressing and traumatic situations. Once, having worked in various hospitals, she transferred to the hospital barges where she claimed there were serious problems of ventilation, particularly when gas casualties were being transported.

Undoubtedly one of the greatest drawbacks to the barges was the want of windows in the sides, which would not only have given us more light and air. This lack of air became most apparent during the last few months of the war ... This was especially so if the load consisted of gassed cases, for, notwithstanding the fact that they were supposed to be washed all over, and have their gassed uniforms removed in hospital, they still seemed to constantly exude the smell of the gas, their breath being especially foul. Frequently, also, they were badly burned, and covered with huge watery blisters, which, when burst, seemed to smell badly. More than once, after evacuating such a load, I have felt quite 'gassed' myself, with sore eyes, sickness, and difficulty in breathing, similar symptoms being shown by other members of the staff.

As will be readily understood, the nursing of the patients in these crowded conditions was very difficult ... However, I am thankful to say that I never lost any of my patients en route, though we sometimes had a hard fight to keep them alive. I feel that I must pay a tribute to those patients of ours, for they seldom grumbled, but bore pain and discomfort with wonderful courage, patience, and cheerfulness. And this gratitude for anything that we did for them was surely reward enough for any trouble we had.

At the beginning of the war, Evelyn Luard, Catherine Black, and Millicent Peterkin were part of a small cadre of professionally trained nurses who, like most others, believed the war would be over in weeks. As the war escalated, demand for proper casualty care soon altered their perception. Between 1914 and 1918 an estimated 24,000 trained nurses were on active service. Professional nurses oversaw the care and treatment of the sick and wounded in 637,746 hospital beds in Britain, Ireland, France and Flanders, and other theatres of war. Their work was supported by 900 nurses on the hospital ships.

Their experiences were far from mundane or predictable as they participated in and contributed to the remarkable developments in medicine and nursing that war had necessitated.

Out of the evils and heartbreak of war, the millions of dead, and many millions more physically and psychologically disabled, future generations were to benefit from significant research and pioneering work carried out in the fields of infection and the control of infection, blood transfusion, bone and skin grafting, X-rays, heart and lung conditions. Care and treatment centres were established for the management and rehabilitation of conditions of the nervous system, and orthopaedic injuries. New mobility devices were pioneered; splints and supports were specially designed for broken bones or paralysed limbs. Under the tuition of an expert, the limbless quite often made their own artificial limbs.

Model farms were developed to help with physical and psychological rehabilitation, physiotherapy was pioneered as well as occupational and speech therapy. Homeopathy, massage, aromatherapy and colour therapy were all employed in the care and treatment of mental and physical wounds and there were developments in audiology when a nurse working with patients from the Royal Artillery invented the first piece of apparatus to detect loss of hearing. There were many innovations and inventions by nurses throughout the period of the war, but sadly they were given little credit for them.

Nevertheless, during the Great War, the nursing profession came into its own and the women of that time were, by any standards, quite exceptional. They were modest and unassuming about their contribution to the war, they did not seek plaudits and they nursed because heart and conscience defied any other action.

In 1919, Douglas Haig wrote of the nurses' contribution to the war:

No survey of the features of war would be complete without some reference to the part played by women serving with the British Armies in France ... The Nursing Sisters of the Canadian Army Medical Corps, and of the Australian, New Zealand, South Africa and Territorial Force Nursing Service and the British Red Cross have maintained and embellished a fine tradition of loyalty and efficiency. Those services have been reinforced by members of the Voluntary Aid Detachments from the British Isles, the Overseas Dominions and the United States of America, who have vied with their professional sisters in cheerfully enduring fatigue in times of stress and gallantly facing danger and death.

Women in the British Red Cross Society and other organisations have driven ambulances throughout the war, undeterred by discomfort and hardship.

Haig's statement failed to convey the depth of involvement that nurses had in various theatres of conflict and not just in France. It said nothing of nursing enterprise or the profession's pioneering work throughout the war. It also failed to recognise the positive effects and value that nursing had on the morale of the sick and injured troops at home and abroad. Sadly, it was totally lacking in reference to the personal sacrifices that nurses made between 1914 and 1918.

In 1919, although women over the age of thirty received the franchise and the nursing profession secured The Nurses Registration Act 1919, internal politics fragmented the profession.

While there had been regular demands for recognition of the profession throughout the war years in the pages of the professional nursing journals the nursing leadership made no attempt to record the nurses' war-time endeavours and sacrifices. The leadership did not see fit to compile a Roll of Honour for those who gave their lives so generously. An incomplete list of names was all that remained in the nursing archives and the deaths of 378 nurses went unrecorded. There were few, if any, commemorations and only a handful of memorials were commissioned, but not by the nurses leaders. It had been suggested in a sermon given in June 1918 by the Bishop of Kensington that 'after the war is over some great national memorial might be established for the nurses who laid down their lives'. This did not happen because nursing leaders were still more interested in securing the status of professional nurses rather than commissioning memorials to commemorate their war legacy. This denial of the lives and deaths of probably the last real pioneers of professional nursing was a cruel omission by the nursing leadership. Their attitude raises many questions ...

\* Did they know or care that, between 1914 and 1918, 378 nurses lost their lives, the youngest to die being 17 and the oldest 54?

\* Were they aware of the number of nurses awarded the Military Medal for 'Bravery and Devotion to Duty'?

\* Did they know the number Mentioned in Dispatches?

\* Did they care about the severe economic hardship that many war disabled nurses suffered and were they aware that economic hardship caused one homeless, emaciated nurse to be found dead in a shop doorway, clutching her war medals?

\* Did they know that psychologically traumatised nurses were often sent back home to the care of their families and that, in one instance, elderly parents had to wash, feed and dress their daughter just as they had done forty years earlier?

\* Were they aware that, when incapacitated through their war experiences, nurses were subjected to the same harsh treatment by the Ministry of Pensions as the physically and psychologically disabled soldiers, sailors and airmen who hoped their country would be grateful enough to grant them a disability pension?

\* Did the record show that Sister Luard spent four years at war despite losing her brother in 1915, was awarded the Royal Red Cross (First Class) for 'Distinguished Service in the Field', and was twice Mentioned in Dispatches.

\* Who knew that Sister Black, returning to a much changed and troubled Ireland – which 16 of her Irish colleagues did not live to see – was subsequently appointed as the personal nurse of King George V?

\* Was anyone aware that Sister Peterkin returned to the Royal Infirmary of Edinburgh and spent the rest of her professional life working there? (Dying in the late 70s, she donated her war diary to the Imperial War Museum, but it appears her family did not know of its existence until 2002.)

Having secured state registration, the profession forgot the enterprise and endurance of the professional nurses, who through their war time endeavours. probably helped to secure the Nurses Registration Act. Like the ether they had been taught to administer, the memory of their compassion and sacrifices evaporated almost immediately. Somehow, over the past ninety years, the nursing profession, the public and historians have managed to ignore the remarkable contributions made to the war effort by professional nurses. The public's attitude was surprising since many thousands of mothers, fathers, wives, brothers and sisters would have been glad to know that their sick or injured men folk were being well taken care of. Many men survived because of the skill, care and encouragement of nurses. It would surely have been deeply distressing for the millions of men they tended to know that the women with whom they shared danger, hardship and esprit de corps, had been denied a grateful and respectful place in the heart of the nation, and the history of the Great War.

If the wartime contribution of professional nurses had been valued by the nursing leadership, a nursing history of the period should and could have been commissioned. If nurses had been encouraged to write about their experiences it might have contributed to the professional and political development of the profession. But for those who served, it was, perhaps, too hard to walk into the light when, for such a long time, the mind had dealt with the darkness of war, and the heart lived in its shadow.

Catherine Black probably spoke for many when she reflected:

It is only on looking back on those years I wonder how I managed to get through them. I know they changed us. You could not go through the things we went through, see the things we saw, and remain the same. You went into it young and light-hearted. You came out older than any span of years could make you.

It is to nurses like Catherine Black, Evelyn Luard, and Millicent Peterkin, that we are indebted. They left us, in their humanity, a history of women in war.

Let us remember the courage, compassion, and endurance of our grandmothers, mothers and aunts who, for four and a half years, nursed our grandfathers, fathers and brothers. Let us never forget all who gave up their health and their lives – for it was hard.

'When this bloody war is over': the now all too familiar sight of the 'Boys in Blue'. *(Courtesy Smith Collection)*

# Postscript

In 1921, the *British Journal of Nursing* carried a feature called 'Why We Study Nursing History' in which it claimed:

> No occupation can be quite intelligently followed or correctly understood unless it is, at least to some extent, illuminated by the light of history … The nurse who knows only her own time and surroundings is not only deprived of an unfailing source of interest, she may also be unable to estimate and judge correctly the current events whose tendency is likely to affect her own career. We must know how the work of nursing arose; what lines it has followed and under what direction it has best developed.

By 1939 when the Second World War was declared, professional nurses had apparently forgotten or were willing to ignore their Great War history. Professional concerns and grievances regarding status, staffing, recruitment, retention and remuneration were revisited, and status issues were once again to the fore and dominating debates. Wartime emergencies saw auxiliary and VAD nurses supplement the work of military and civilian nurses, re-kindling the old animosity between professional and untrained nurses regarding post-war employment.

In spite of the concerns voiced so often in the professional nursing journals, after the First World War, VAD nurses did not swamp the labour market and deprive trained nurses of regular employment. Nothing was further from the truth. There had been a shortage of nurses throughout the war and that situation continued for many years after the Armistice because the toll taken by the war reduced the ability of some to work, and others could not join the labour market as they had to care for their returning relatives.

Recruitment, staffing and salary issues brought professional nurses into conflict with the government. The nursing press fulminated about the erosion of nurses' status and the use of 'bath attendants' to care for the sick and injured, claiming it was 'incredible that totally ignorant Ministers of the Crown should be permitted to smash up, not only the status of an honourable profession, but deprive the public of the necessary safeguards to health and life.' Thirty years earlier the profession had engaged in the same shroud-waving rhetoric to protect its interests. In spite of Great War experiences and the battle for professional recognition, few lessons, if any, had been learned.

In the course of researching nursing archives for this book, old issues and themes surfaced repeatedly: status and rivalry for example. There is a cycle of professional insecurity in the history of nursing, and the frequent debates among nursing analysts, educators and observers over a perceived 'crisis of confidence' or 'crisis of meaning'. Perhaps the 'crisis', if it exists, is one of professional identity.

Some contemporary commentators have concluded that the nursing profession lacks power and that, in effect, it is a semi-profession. Others have questioned the motives of nurses seeking professionalisation and others use the gender-feminist argument to support their contention that women are exploited as nurses because they are socialised into the female role, equating nursing with mothering.

The characterisation of nurses as perpetually politically weak needs to be addressed by the profession and, to understand the status of nursing, the profession might wish to reflect on questions relating to its historical identity. Are professional debates lost to emotive rhetoric instead of historical analysis? How many nursing representatives have gone to the negotiating table or policy meetings with a portfolio of evidence of professional nurses' achievements? What, for example, has the profession inherited or acquired throughout its history that may be detrimental or advantageous to its political and social progress? What value does the nursing profession place on its historical identity and how does the use of history allow the profession to measure its progress and effectiveness? Will it be left to sociologists, health analysts and general historians to comment on the history of the profession's achievements and failures, or are nurses willing to analyse their contribution to society? Why are nurses reluctant to recognise their importance as custodians of their own history?

Professional nurses have witnessed and practised in some of the most spectacular survival-testing historical events of the nineteenth and twentieth centuries. Had the profession been more aware of its wartime historical identity and achievements, it might have been recognised as the foremost authority on trauma care, rehabilitation and 'survivor' issues – but it was not until the 1980s that the profession chose to have any input into trauma care development. Today, the nursing profession, whether through choice or politics, has taken a back seat on survivor education. The issues around survivorship now appear to be left to the disciplines of psychology, psychiatry and the controversial practice of counselling.

One can only speculate why the nursing profession, with its vast practical experience of dealing with people in crisis, has come to believe that other disciplines can offer more in the understanding of survivorship. In the absence of self-belief or because of a crisis of identity, the reality is that hard-earned insight, experience and expertise, much of it gained in two world wars, have been ignored, and relinquished.

The medical innovations that arose as a consequence of war were a turning point in the history of medicine and nursing. Developments in wound management, infection control, blood transfusion, resuscitation, anaesthetics, reconstructive surgery, and rehabilitation were just some of the results of pioneering work carried out during modern warfare, with the nursing profession at the forefront of much of the research and its implementation. Sadly, little is known of the many innovative contributions by nurses. The concepts of homeopathy, massage, aromatherapy and colour therapy as forms of treatment are now being used as 'innovative practices' in some areas of nursing, despite being pioneered by professional nurses ninety years ago. During the Great War, a small group of professional nurses was trained in the use and administration of anaesthetics; sixty years later this was introduced as 'pioneering new practice'. Had the nursing profession kept faith with its wartime innovations and enterprise, there could have been even more remarkable contributions to today's patient care. Unfortunately, professional nurses forgot what they had pioneered and learned.

The historian Carr wrote, 'There is no more significant pointer to the character of a society than the kind of history it writes – or fails to write.' This provides us with a moral compass by reminding us why history is important. Why has there been a failure within the nursing profession to examine and record its contribution at times of national crisis? Arguably, the profession, society and history are poorer for it.

# Bibliography

**General References**
Locations of Casualty Clearing Stations, BEF, 1914–1918, Ministry of Pensions, HMSO 1923.
Mitchell J, Smith G M, Casualties and Medical Statistics of The Great War, HMSO 1931.
Official Histories of the Great War: Medical Services, HMSO 1923.
The Times Diary and Index of the War, 1914–1918, J B Hayward and Son 1985.
Report of the War Office Committee of Enquiry Into 'Shell-Shock' 1922.

**Primary Sources**
Allen Library, Dublin (Rebellion Papers, Witness Statements).
Army Roll of Honour (Officers Died WW1).
Commonwealth War Graves Commission (Data Base – Women Who Died in the First World War).
Doherty Papers (Private Collection).
General Register of Scotland (The 'Minor Records').
Imperial War Museum (Peterkin, Clarke, Georgine and Bickmore Diaries and Papers).
Isabel Smith Collection (Private Papers and Photographs).
McArdle-Broadley (Private Papers).
McEwen-Doherty Collection (Miscellaneous Private Papers and Medals Collection).
National Army Museum (Papers of Lord Roberts, 1971-01-23).
National Library Ireland (Rebellion Papers, Witness Statements).
National Library Scotland (Chisholm Papers, Acc 8066).
Public Record Office of Northern Ireland (Maxwell Papers, D/3226/16 & 20).
Royal College of Nursing Archives (*The Nursing Record, The Nursing Times, the British Journal of Nursing*).
The National Archives (PIN26, WO158, WO32, WO95, MH1060).
The University of Edinburgh (Special Collections Department, Lothian Health Archive, Peterkin Papers).

**Newspapers and Journals**
*British Journal of Nursing*
*Daily Chronicle*
*Daily Sketch*
*Freeman's Journal*
*Le Petit Journal*
*Liverpool Daily Post*
*The Belfast Newsletter*

*The Birmingham Weekly Post*
*The British Medical Journal*
*The Catholic Bulletin*
*The Daily Mail*
*The Globe*
*The Illustrated London News*
*The Irish Sword*
*The Irish Times*
*The Lancet*
*The Nursing Mirror and Midwives Journal*
*The Nursing Record*
*The Nursing Times*
*The Scotsman*
*The Sheffield Daily Telegraph*
*The Star*
*The Times*
*War Pensions Gazette*

(Unless otherwise stated, all books are published in London)

## Biography / Autobiography
Barbusse, Henri, *Under Fire,* Penguin 2003.
Black, Catherine, *Kings Nurse Beggars Nurse,* Hurst and Blackett 1930
Bowser, Thelka, *The story of the VAD Work in the Great War,* Andrew Melrose 1917.
Chapman-Huston D. and Rutter O., *General Sir John Cowans*, Hutchinson and Company 1924.
Coppard, George, *With a Machine Gun to Cambrai*, Cassell 1999.
Dent, Olive, *A VAD in France*, Grant Richards Ltd 1917.
Eyre, Giles E. M., *Somme Harvest*, London Stamp Exchange Ltd 1991
Gibbs, Philip, *Now It Can Be Told*, Harper and Brothers 1920.
Gibbs, Philip, *The Realities of War,* Heinemann 1920.
Lloyd George, David, *War Memoirs,* Odhams 1938.
Luard K. E., *Unknown Warriors*, Chatto and Windus 1930.
Lucy J., *There's a Devil in the Drum*, The Naval and Military Press 1992.
MacGill, Partrick, *The Great Push,* Birlinn Ltd 2000.
Montague, C. E., *Disenchantment*, Evergreen Books 1940.
O'Rahilly, Alfred, *Father William Doyle SJ*, Longmans, Green and Co. 1922.
Pankhurst, Emmiline, *My Own Story,* Eveleigh Nash 1914.
Plowman, Max, *A Subaltern on the Somme*, Battery Press 1927.
Purdom C. B., *Everyman at War,* Purdom 1930.
Richards, Frank, *Old Soldiers Never Die*, Faber and Faber 1933
Sanderson, E., Melville, L, *King Edward VII*, Gresham Publishing Company 1910.
Soutter H. S., *A Surgeon in Belgium,* Edward Arnold 1915.

Terraine, John (ed), *General Jack's Diary*, Cassell 1964.

## General Social and Military History Books

Adleman P., *The Rise of the Labour Party 1880–1945*, Longman 1996.

Ashworth T. *Trench Warfare*, Pan Books 1980.

Babington, A, *Shell-shock: a History of Changing Attitudes to War Neurosis*, Leo Cooper 1997.

Baynes, John, *Morale,* Cassell and Company Ltd. 1967.

Brown, M, *The Imperial War Museum Book of the First World War*, Sedgwick and Jackson 1991.

Brown, M, *Verdun – 1916*, Tempus Publishing Limited, 1999.

Carew, Tim, *The Vanished Army,* Corgi 1971.

Churchill W., *The World Crisis*, Butterworth 1933.

Clark, Alan, *The Donkeys,* Mayflower 1961.

Cuddeford G. M., *Women in Society*, Hamish Hamilton 1976.

Dunn J. C., *The War the Infantry Knew 1914–1919*, Abacus 1987.

Edward Crankshaw, *The Fall of the House of Habsburg*, Sphere Books 1963.

Hamilton, R., *The War Diary of the Master of Belhaven,* John Murray 1924.

Harris J., *The Somme: Death of a Generation*, Zenith 1966.

Horne, Alistair, *The Price of Glory – Verdun 1916,* MacMillan 1962.

Keegan J., Holmes R, *Soldiers: A History of Men in Battle*, Hamish Hamilton 1985.

Keegan, John, *The Face of Battle*, Pimlico 1991.

Keegan J., *The First World War,* Hutchinson 1998.

Laffin J., *The Western Front*, Sutton Publishing Limited 1997.

Lawrence J., *Warrior Race: A History of the British at War*, Little, Brown and Company 2001.

Leneman L., *In The Service of Life,* Mercat Press 1994.

Liddell Hart B., *History of the First World War*, Cassell 1970.

McGann S., *The Battle of the Nurses,* Scutari 1992.

McLaren B., *Women of the War*, Hodder and Stoughton 1917.

Masefield, J., *The Old Front Line*, Heinemann 1917

Middlebrook, Martin, *The First Day of the Somme*, Penguin Books 1984.

Moore W., *Gas Attack*, Leo Cooper 1987.

Moran, Lord, *The Anatomy of Courage*, Constable and Company Ltd 1945.

*Mr Punch's History of the Great War,* Cassell 1919.

Oldfield S., *Women Humanitarians*, Continuum 2001.

Peel C. S., *How We Lived Then*, John Lane 1929.

Pike E. R., *The Trade Unions, Welfare and the Individual in 1914,* Odhams 1967.

Shephard B., *A War of Nerves*, Jonathan Cape 2000.

Shinwell E., *The Labour Story*, MacDonald and Company 1963.

Simpson, A., *The Evolution of Victory*, Tom Donovan Publishing, 1995.

Taylor A. J. P., *The First World War*, Penguin 1966.

Taylor, A. J. P., *From Sarajevo to Potsdam*, Thames and Hudson, 1966

Terraine J., *The Great War*, Hutchinson 1965.

Terraine, John, *Mons,* Pan Books 1972.

*The First World War,* Daily Express Publications 1933.

*The Life and Times of King GeorgeV,* Odhams 1937.

Vansittart, P., *Voices from the Great War,* Pimlico 1998.

Whitehead I., *Doctors in the Great War,* Leo Cooper 1999.

Williams, John, *The Home Fronts,* Constable and Company Limited 1972.

Wilson H. W., Hammerton J A, (eds), *The Great War (1915-1919),* Amalgamated Press Limited.

Winter, Denis, *Death's Men,* Penguin 1978.

Winter, Denis, *Haig's Command,* Penguin 1991.

## Books on Ireland

*1916 Rebellion Handbook,* Dublin 1998.

Bartlett, Thomas and Jeffery, Keith, *A Military History of Ireland,* Cambridge University Press 1996.

Bredin, Brigadier A. E. C., *A History of The Irish Soldier,* Century Books 1987.

Denman, Terence, *Ireland's Unknown Soldiers,* Irish Academic Press, Dublin 1992.

Foster R. F., *Modern Ireland 1600–1972,* Penguin Books 1989.

Fox R. M., *A History of the Irish Citizen Army,* Dublin 1944.

Harris G., *The Irish Regiments,* Spellmount 1989.

Jeffrey, Keith, *Ireland and the Great War,* Cambridge University Press 2002.

Johnstone Tom, *Orange Green and Khaki,* Gill and MacMillan 1992.

Kee, Robert, *The Green Flag Vol.1–3,* Penguin 1972.

Kee, Robert, *Ireland a History,* Weidenfield & Nicolson Ltd 1980.

Lee, Joseph, *Ireland 1912 to 1985 – Politics and Society,* Cambridge University Press 1989.

Lyons, J. B., *The Enigma of Tom Kettle,* The Glendale Press, Dublin,

MacDonagh, Michael, *The Irish on the Front,* Hodder and Stoughton 1916.

MacManus, Séamus, *The Story of the Irish Race,* Devlin Adair 1921.

Stewart A. T. Q., *Carson,* The Blackstaff Press Ltd 1997.

# Roll of Honour

## Nurses of the Great War – Deaths

**Abbreviations**

CBE:      Commander of the British Empire
CdGP:    Croix de Guerre with Palms
CM:       The Cross of Mercy (Serbia)
MiD:      Mentioned in Despatches
NIM:      Nightingale International Medal
NK:       Not Known
OStJ:     Order of St John of Jerusalem
RRCM:    Royal Red Cross Medal
SMDS:    Silver Medal for Devoted Service in War (Serbia)

### Australian Army Nursing Service

| Name | Age | Status | Cause of Death | Date | Distinction |
|------|-----|--------|----------------|------|-------------|
| Bicknell L. A. | NK | Staff Nurse | Sickness | 25/06/15 | |
| Brennan K. A. | NK | Nurse | NK | 24/11/18 | |
| Clare E. | 28 | Sister | NK | 17/10/18 | |
| Dickinson R. | 32 | Staff Nurse | NK | 23/06/18 | |
| Grewar G. E. | NK | Sister | NK | 24/05/21 | |
| Hennessy M. | NK | Staff Nurse | NK | 09/04/19 | |
| Knox H. M. | 33 | Sister | Sickness | 17/02/17 | |
| McPhail I. | NK | Staff Nurse | NK | 04/08/20 | |
| Moorhouse E. A. | 33 | Sister | Sickness | 24/11/18 | |
| Moreton L. G. | 26 | Sister | Enteric | 11/11/16 | |
| Mowbray N. V. | 32 | Staff Nurse | Pneumonia | 21/01/16 | |
| Munro G. E. | 36 | Sister | Sickness | 10/09/18 | |
| O'Grady A. V. | NK | Sister | NK | 12/08/16 | |
| O'Kane R. | 28 | Staff Nurse | NK | 21/12/18 | |
| Porter K. A. L. | NK | Sister | NK | 16/07/19 | MiD |
| Power K. | 28 | Sister | NK | 13/08/16 | |
| Ridgway D. A. | NK | Staff Nurse | NK | 06/01/19 | |
| Rothery E. | 33 | Staff Nurse | NK | 15/06/18 | |
| Stafford M. F. | 27 | Staff Nurse | NK | 19/03/19 | |
| Thomson A. M. | NK | Staff Nurse | NK | 01/01/19 | |
| Tyson F. I. C. | 28 | Sister | Sickness | 20/04/19 | |
| Walker J. M. | 39 | Matron | Sickness | 30/10/18 | |
| Watson B. M. | 34. | Staff Nurse | Sickness | 02/06/16 | |
| Williams B. E. | 38 | Sister | NK | 24/05/20 | |

### British Red Cross Society

| Name | Age | Status | Cause of Death | Date | Distinction |
|------|-----|--------|----------------|------|-------------|
| Craggs M. O. | NK | Nurse | NK | 20/01/15 | |
| Warnock E. McM. | 31 | Nurse | Septicaemia | 05/05/18 | |

### Canadian Army Medical Corps

| Name | Age | Status | Cause of Death | Date | Distinction |
|------|-----|--------|----------------|------|-------------|
| Alpaugh A. | 26 | Sister | Pneumonia | 12/10/18 | |
| Baker M. E. | NK | Sister | NK | 17/10/18 | |
| Baker M. E. | 45 | Sister | Sickness | 30/05/19 | |

## Canadian Army Medical Corps (cont.)

| Bolton G. E. | 28 | Nurse | NK | 16/02/19 | |
|---|---|---|---|---|---|
| Campbell C. | 45 | Sister | Drowned *Llandovery* | 27/06/18 | |
| Champagne E. | NK | Nurse | Phthisis | 24/03/19 | |
| Cumming I. | 41 | Sister | Phthisis | 04/02/21 | |
| Dagg A. St. C. | 26 | Sister | Sickness | 29/11/18 | |
| Donaldson G. | 25 | Sister | NK | 29/07/19 | |
| Douglas C. J. | NK | Sister | Drowned *Llandovery* | 27/06/18 | |
| Dussault A. | NK | Sister | Drowned *Llandovery* | 27/06/18 | |
| Follette M. A. | NK | Sister | Drowned *Llandovery* | 27/06/18 | |
| Forneri A. F. | 39 | Sister | NK | 24/04/18 | |
| Fortescue M. J. | NK | Sister | Drowned *Llandovery* | 27/06/18 | |
| Fraser M. M. | 34 | Sister | Drowned *Llandovery* | 27/06/18 | |
| Frederickson C. | 22 | Sister | Pneumonia | 28/10/18 | |
| Gallaher M. K. | NK | Sister | Drowned *Llandovery* | 27/06/18 | |
| Grant G. M. | 35 | Sister | Nephritis | 12/09/19 | |
| Hennan V. B. | 31 | Sister | NK | 23/10/18 | |
| Henshaw I. | 50 | Sister | Sickness | 11/08/19 | |
| Hunt M. | 28 | Sister | Pneumonia | 16/01/18 | |
| Jaggard J. B. | 44 | Matron | NK | 25/09/15 | |
| Jarvis J. | 29 | Sister | Pneumonia | 23/05/18 | |
| Jenner L. M. | 29 | Sister | NK | 12/12/18 | |
| Kealy I. L. | 39 | Sister | Pneumonia | 12/03/18 | |
| King J. N. | NK | Sister | NK | 04/04/19 | |
| MacIntosh R. | 25 | Sister | Pneumonia | 07/03/19 | |
| MacLeod M. | 39 | Sister | Phthisis | 20/12/19 | |
| McDiarmid J. M. | NK | Sister | Drowned *Llandovery* | 27/06/18 | |
| McDougall A. | 48 | Sister | NK | 18/07/19 | |
| McEachen R. | 33 | Sister | Meningitis | 16/11/18 | |
| McGinnis M. G. | 27 | Sister | NK | 10/02/20 | |
| McKay E. V. | 27 | Sister | NK | 04/11/18 | |
| McKenzie M. A. | 40 | Sister | Drowned *Llandovery* | 27/06/18 | |
| McLean R. M. | 38 | Sister | Drowned *Llandovery* | 27/06/18 | |
| Mellett H. | 39 | Sister | Drowned *Leinster* | 10/10/18 | |
| Munro M. F. E. | NK | Sister | NK | 07/09/15 | |
| Roberts J. | 32 | Sister | Influenza | 03/11/18 | |
| Rogers N. G. | 29 | Sister | NK | 19/10/18 | |
| Ross A. J. | 50 | Sister | NK | 12/07/18 | |
| Ross E. G. | NK | Sister | Pneumonia | 26/02/16 | |
| Sampson M. B. | 28 | Sister | Drowned *Llandovery* | 27/06/18 | MiD |
| Sare G. I. | NK | Sister | Drowned *Llandovery* | 27/06/18 | |
| Sparks E. | NK | Sister | NK | 20/08/17 | |
| Stamers A. I. | 30 | Sister | Drowned *Llandovery* | 27/06/18 | |
| Templeman J. | 33 | Sister | Drowned *Llandovery* | 27/06/18 | |
| Trusdale A. | NK | Sister | Sickness | 12/09/19 | |
| Tupper A. A. | NK | Sister | NK | 09/12/16 | |

## Canadian Army Nursing Service

| Name | Age | Status | Cause of Death | Date | Distinction |
|---|---|---|---|---|---|
| Baldwin G. | NK | Sister | Died of wounds | 30/05/18 | |
| Davis L. A. | NK | Sister | NK | 21/02/18 | |
| Garbutt S. E. | NK | Sister | NK | 20/08/17 | |
| Green M. | 32 | Sister | Disease | 09/10/18 | |
| Lowe M. | 32 | Sister | Died of wounds | 28/05/18 | |
| MacDonald K. M. | 31 | Sister | Died of wounds | 19/05/18 | |

## Canadian Army Nursing Service (cont.)

| | | | | | |
|---|---|---|---|---|---|
| MacPherson A. | NK | Sister | Died of wounds | 30/05/18 | |
| Pringle E. L. | 25 | Sister | Died of wounds | 30/05/18 | |
| Wake G. M. M. | 34 | Sister | Died of wounds | 21/05/18 | |
| Whitely A. | NK | Sister | NK | 21/04/18 | |

## First Aid Nursing Yeomanry

| Name | Age | Status | Cause of Death | Date | Distinction |
|---|---|---|---|---|---|
| Shaw E. F. | NK | Nurse | NK | 24/08/18 | CdGP |

## New Zealand Army Nursing Service

| Name | Age | Status | Cause of Death | Date | Distinction |
|---|---|---|---|---|---|
| Brown M. S. | NK | Staff Nurse | Drowned *Marquette* | 23/10/15 | |
| Clark I. | NK | Staff Nurse | Drowned Marquette | 23/10/15 | |
| Fox C. A. | NK | Staff Nurse | Drowned *Marquette* | 23/10/15 | |
| Gilbert Hawken A. | NK | Staff Nurse | Enteric | 18/10/15 | |
| Gorman M. | NK | Staff Nurse | Drowned *Marquette* | 23/10/15 | |
| Hildyard N. M. | 28 | Staff Nurse | Drowned *Marquette* | 23/10/15 | |
| Isdell H. K. | NK | Staff Nurse | Drowned *Marquette* | 23/10/15 | |
| Jamieson M. E. | NK | Staff Nurse | Drowned *Marquette* | 23/10/15 | |
| Lumley C. | NK | Nurse | NK | 25/11/18 | |
| Rae M. H. | 36 | Staff Nurse | Drowned *Marquette* | 23/10/15 | |
| Rattray L. A. | NK | Staff Nurse | Drowned *Marquette* | 23/10/15 | |
| Rogers M | NK | Staff Nurse | Drowned *Marquette* | 23/10/15 | |
| Thompson M. H. | 36 | Staff Nurse | NK | 28/02/21 | |
| Tubman E. M. | 31 | Staff Nurse | NK | 18/09/18 | |
| Whishaw M. H. | NK | Sister | Influenza | 10/11/18 | |

## Nyasaland Nursing Service

| Name | Age | Status | Cause of Death | Date | Distinction |
|---|---|---|---|---|---|
| Salvator | NK | Sister | NK | 08/09/18 | |

## Queen Alexandra's Imperial Military Nursing Service

| Name | Age | Status | Cause of Death | Date | Distinction |
|---|---|---|---|---|---|
| Armstrong E. R. R. | 38 | Sister | NK | 20/03/19 | MiD |
| Allen M. A. | 35 | Staff Nurse | Malaria | 05/01/20 | |
| Bates F. M. | NK | Probationer | NK | 09/04/16 | |
| Beaufoy K. | NK | Matron | Drowned *Glenart* | 26/02/18 | |
| Bennet H. S. | NK | Staff Nurse | NK | 18/10/18 | |
| Beresford R. R. | 39 | Staff Nurse | Drowned *Glenart* | 26/02/18 | |
| Bird L. E. | 29 | Staff Nurse | Heart failure | 19/08/19 | |
| Blake E. | 32 | Staff Nurse | Drowned *Glenart* | 26/02/18 | |
| Bode-Blandy S. R. | NK | Sister | NK | 13/01/19 | |
| Bolger K. | 30 | Staff Nurse | Pneumonia | 05/03/16 | |
| Bond E. M. | 31 | Sister | NK | 03/11/18 | |
| Brown E. L. | NK | Sister | NK | 19/02/19 | |
| Buckingham M. A. | 42 | Matron | NK | 04/12/15 | |
| Buckler A. E. | 43 | Staff Nurse | Influenza | 17/10/18 | |
| Butler S. E. | NK | Sister | NK | 14/04/16 | |
| Callier E. F. M. C. | NK | Sister | NK | 22/06/19 | |
| Challinor E. A. | 29 | Staff Nurse | Pneumonia | 26/10/18 | |
| Chandler D. M. | 31 | Sister | NK | 15/11/17 | |

## Queen Alexandra's Imperial Military Nursing Service (cont.)

| Cole E. H. | 32 | Sister | NK | 21/02/15 | |
|---|---|---|---|---|---|
| Compton F. D | 29 | Sister | Drowned | 15/01/18 | |
| Consterdine V. C. | NK | Staff Nurse | NK | 06/11/18 | |
| Cooke E. K. | NK | Staff Nurse | NK | 08/09/17 | |
| Cooper A. | 38 | Sister | NK | 17/11/19 | MiD |
| Corfield A. B. | NK | Sister | NK | 02/02/16 | |
| Crowther L. | NK | Sister | NK | 22/10/16 | |
| Croysdale M. | 26 | Sister | NK | 02/03/19 | |
| Cruickshank I. | 48 | Sister | Lost at sea *Salta* | 10/04/17 | |
| Dalton J. G. | NK | Sister | NK | 20/03/16 | |
| Dawes A. E. | NK | Sister | NK | 23/10/18 | |
| Dawson E. M. | 49 | Matron | NK | 10/04/17 | |
| Dewar M. | NK | Staff Nurse | NK | 12/03/17 | |
| Doherty M. A. | 28 | Sister | Dysentery | 05/09/16 | MiD, RRCM |
| Donovan B. | NK | Staff Nurse | NK | 03/04/16 | |
| Duckers M. E. | 25 | Staff Nurse | NK | 16/05/18 | |
| Duncan I. L. M. | NK | Sister | NK | 01/03/17 | |
| Edgar E. | NK | Staff Nurse | Drowned *Glenart* | 26/02/18 | |
| Elliffe M. | 27 | Sister | NK | 24/05/16 | |
| Evans J. | NK | Sister | Drowned *Glenart* | 26/02/18 | |
| Fearnley E. | NK | Staff Nurse | NK | 23/11/14 | |
| Foyster E. L. | 36 | Sister | Lost at sea *Salta* | 10/04/17 | |
| Garner A. E. C. | NK | Sister | NK | 12/03/17 | |
| Gladstone E. M. | 32 | Sister | Pneumonia | 24/01/19 | |
| Gorbutt M. | NK | Sister | NK | 28/07/20 | |
| Griffiths J. L. | NK | Sister | NK | 30/10/15 | |
| Grover A. J. | 43 | Sister | Pneumonia | 06/02/19 | |
| Gurney E. S. | NK | Staff Nurse | Lost at sea *Salta* | 10/04/17 | |
| Hall F. M. | 45 | Matron | NK | 07/07/19 | MiD |
| Hannaford I. D. | 34 | Staff Nurse | NK | 14/03/18 | |
| Harrison W. M. | NK | Sister | NK | 03/04/20 | |
| Hawley F. | 29 | Staff Nurse | NK | 20/06/18 | |
| Hawley N. | 29 | Probationer | Drowned *Osmanieh* | 31/12/17 | |
| Henry C. E. | NK | Staff Nurse | Drowned *Glenart* | 26/02/18 | |
| Hetterley H. | 26 | Staff Nurse | NK | 30/05/17 | |
| Hilling S. | 34 | Sister | Pneumonia | 12/10/18 | |
| Hockey J. O. | 32 | Sister | NK | 14/08/17 | |
| Hodgson E. M. | NK | Sister | Malaria | 21/12/18 | |
| Hook F. M. L. | NK | Ass. Nurse | NK | 10/11/18 | |
| Hughes G. C. | NK | Staff Nurse | NK | 06/11/18 | |
| Jack C. | 35 | Sister | NK | 22/10/18 | |
| Johnson A. M. | 24 | Sister | Sickness | 24/10/18 | |
| Jones B. I. | 54 | Chief Matron | NK | 14/01/21 | CBE, NIM |
| Jones G. E. | 31 | Sister | Lost at sea *Salta* | 10/04/17 | |
| Jones L. H. | 32 | Sister | Pneumonia | 28/10/18 | |
| Kearney I. M. | NK | Sister | NK | 26/09/16 | |
| Kemp C. M. F. | NK | Staff Nurse | NK | 04/07/18 | |
| Kendall R. E. | 31 | Sister | Drowned *Glenart* | 26/02/18 | |
| MacBeth M. A. | 28 | Staff Nurse | NK | 30/10/18 | |
| MacGill M. M. | 32 | Matron | NK | 11/03/15 | |
| MacKenzie I. | NK | Nurse | NK | 02/11/18 | |
| Mann A. G. | 25 | Staff Nurse | Lost at sea *Salta* | 10/04/17 | |
| Marmion M. | 37 | Nurse | NK | 25/01/19 | |
| Marshall M. B. | 30 | Staff Nurse | Enemy air raid | 12/03/17 | MiD, CdGP |
| Mason F. | 27 | Staff Nurse | Lost at sea *Salta* | 10/04/17 | |

## Queen Alexandra's Imperial Military Nursing Service (cont.)

| | | | | | |
|---|---|---|---|---|---|
| McGibbon R. A. | NK | Sister | NK | 06/03/19 | |
| McRobbie J. E. | 32 | Nurse | NK | 07/11/18 | |
| Meikle C. | 23 | Nurse | NK | 14/10/18 | |
| Milne H. | 31 | Sister | NK | 23/11/17 | |
| Moreton A. | 38 | Nurse | NK | 07/09/16 | |
| Nicol C. | 34 | Sister | NK | 06/02/17 | |
| O'Brien M. | 31 | Nurse | NK | 21/02/17 | |
| Parker E. K. | NK | Matron | Dysentery | 16/10/16 | |
| Partridge C. H. | 42 | Staff Nurse | Phthisis | 05/01/20 | |
| Pearse P. A. | 28 | Staff Nurse | Neurasthenia | 29/04/15 | |
| Pepper E. D. | 25 | Probationer | NK | 07/04/18 | |
| Phillips J. | NK | Sister | Drowned *Asturias* | 21/03/17 | |
| Pilling D. E. | 24 | Probationer | Pneumonia | 28/03/19 | |
| Radcliffe E. B. | NK | Sister | NK | 10/03/19 | |
| Reid A. C. | 32 | Staff Nurse | NK | 04/03/19 | |
| Ritchie J. | NK | Staff Nurse | NK | 13/08/16 | |
| Roberts E. | NK | Staff Nurse | NK | 12/08/17 | |
| Roberts J. | NK | Staff Nurse | Lost at sea *Salta* | 10/04/17 | |
| Roberts M. D. | NK | Staff Nurse | Drowned *Osmanieh* | 31/12/17 | |
| Robinette C. A. | NK | Staff Nurse | NK | 30/03/17 | |
| Robins M. J. | 28 | Sister | Pneumonia | 04/11/18 | |
| Rodwell M. | NK | Staff Nurse | Drowned *Anglia* | 17/11/15 | |
| Russell A. M. | NK | Staff Nurse | NK | 04/10/16 | |
| Seymour C. E. M. | 29 | Probationer | Meningitis | 12/02/17 | |
| Smith F. E. | NK | Staff Nurse | NK | 01/07/18 | |
| Smith J. B. | 42 | Sister | NK | 28/04/16 | |
| Smith S. M. C. | 37 | Staff Nurse | NK | 12/02/16 | |
| Spindler N. | 26 | Staff Nurse | Killed in action | 21/08/17 | |
| Stacey D. L. | 25 | Staff Nurse | NK | 05/10/18 | |
| Stalker M. B. | NK | Sister | NK | 18/01/21 | |
| Stephenson G. A | 42 | Sister | NK | 25/03/18 | |
| Stevens L. | NK | Staff Nurse | NK | 15/03/16 | |
| Stewart E. G. | NK | Staff Nurse | NK | 15/02/16 | |
| Sturt K. R. | 28 | Staff Nurse | NK | 13/12/16 | |
| Teggin E. E. | 28 | Staff Nurse | NK | 25/12/18 | |
| Thomas L. | 27 | Staff Nurse | NK | 14/08/18 | |
| Thomson E. R. | 36 | Sister | Sickness | 26/10/18 | |
| Tindall F. | NK | Sister | Drowned | 15/01/18 | |
| Townsend M. | NK | Staff Nurse | NK | 21/09/18 | |
| Tulloch E. S. | 33 | Staff Nurse | NK | 08/10/18 | |
| Turton A. M. | 36 | Staff Nurse | Pneumonia | 07/05/17 | |
| Watson E. H. | 30 | Staff Nurse | Pneumonia | 05/11/18 | |
| Wallace L. | NK | Staff Nurse | NK | 06/06/16 | |
| Watson M. | NK | Nurse | NK | 06/11/18 | |
| Welford A. | 30 | Sister | Drowned | 15/01/18 | |
| Williams K. | 38 | Staff Nurse | NK | 04/08/19 | |
| Willson N. | 30 | Staff Nurse | NK | 16/10/18 | |
| Wilson C. M. | 42 | Sister | Pneumonia | 01/03/16 | |
| Wilson M. E. | 38 | Sister | Pneumonia | 23/12/15 | |

## Queen Alexandra's Royal Naval Nursing Service

| Name | Age | Status | Cause of Death | Date | Distinction |
|---|---|---|---|---|---|
| Ainsworth G. G. | NK | Sister | NK | 29/10/18 | |

## Queen Alexandra's Royal Naval Nursing Service (cont.)

| | | | | | |
|---|---|---|---|---|---|
| Beard E. G. | 33 | Sister | NK | 14/03/20 | |
| Chamberlain L. C. | NK | Sister | Mine explosion *China* | 10/08/18 | |
| Edwards C. M. | NK | Sister | Destruction of *Natal* | 30/12/15 | |
| Elvens E. M. | NK | Sister | Destruction of *Natal* | 30/12/15 | |
| Prevost A. M. | NK | Sister | NK | 19/11/18 | |
| Rowlett O. K. | NK | Sister | Destruction of *Natal* | 30/12/15 | |
| Wilson A. | NK | Sister | NK | 05/11/18 | |

## Queen Mary's Army Auxiliary Corps

| Name | Age | Status | Cause of Death | Date | Distinction |
|---|---|---|---|---|---|
| Rathmell E. | 21 | Ass. Matron | Phthisis | 28/07/19 | |

## Royal Navy

| Name | Age | Status | Cause of Death | Date | Distinction |
|---|---|---|---|---|---|
| Grigson M. E. | 36 | Sister | NK | 03/10/18 | |

## Scottish Women's Hospital

| Name | Age | Status | Cause of Death | Date | Distinction |
|---|---|---|---|---|---|
| Burt M. De B. | NK | Sister | Dysentery | 07/04/16 | |
| Caton F. M. | NK | Sister | Appendicitis | 15/07/17 | |
| Earl A. K. | 33 | Sister | Septicaemia | 19/03/19 | CM, SMDS |
| Gray M. | NK | Nurse | Septicaemia | 23/01/16 | |
| Grey A. A. | NK | Sister | NK | 21/08/16 | |
| Jordan L. | 36 | Sister | Typhus | 06/03/15 | |
| Minshull A. M. | NK | Sister | Typhus | 21/04/15 | |
| Sutherland B. G. | 43 | Sister | Enteric | 26/09/15 | |
| Toughill C. M. | NK | Nurse | Killed in action | 14/11/15 | |

## South African Military Nursing Service

| Name | Age | Status | Cause of Death | Date | Distinction |
|---|---|---|---|---|---|
| Baker E. A. | 28 | Staff Nurse | NK | 06/11/18 | |
| Beaufort K. | NK | Nurse | NK | 21/10/18 | |
| Bernstein D. | NK | Staff Nurse | NK | 06/11/18 | |
| Bettle H. M. | 29 | Sister | NK | 07/02/19 | |
| Dunn G. E. | NK | Staff Nurse | NK | 14/12/18 | |
| Edmeades C. A. | 28 | Sister | NK | 17/10/18 | |
| Fitzhenry D. A. | NK | Sister | NK | 01/12/18 | |
| Flanagan M. C. | 30 | Probationer | NK | 29/02/20 | |
| Hearns B. | NK | Staff Nurse | NK | 20/10/18 | |
| Munro A. W. | 26 | Staff Nurse | Phthisis | 06/04/17 | |
| Wardle I. | NK | Staff Nurse | NK | 13/10/18 | |
| Watkins J. K. | NK | Staff Nurse | NK | 21/10/18 | |

## St John's Ambulance Brigade Hospital

| Name | Age | Status | Cause of Death | Date | Distinction |
|---|---|---|---|---|---|
| Bain A. W. | 30 | Sister | Enemy air raid | 01/06/18 | MiD, OStJ |

**Territorial Nursing Service**

| Name | Age | Status | Cause of Death | Date | Distinction |
|---|---|---|---|---|---|
| Andrew E. | 32 | Sister | Enemy air raid | 21/03/18 | |
| Astell F. E. | 38 | Sister | NK | 17/12/17 | |
| Blacklock A. M. | 30 | Sister | NK | 13/08/16 | |
| Blencowe M. E. | 36 | Sister | NK | 10/03/17 | |
| Brett N. V. | NK | Staff Nurse | NK | 20/05/15 | |
| Brinton M. G. | NK | Staff Nurse | NK | 30/10/18 | |
| Cammack E. M. | NK | Staff Nurse | Illness | 01/03/18 | |
| Carley B. | NK | Ass. Matron | NK | 26/04/20 | |
| Climie A. M. | 32 | Staff Nurse | NK | 30/09/17 | |
| Cole D. E. | 29 | Sister | Pneumonia | 24/10/18 | |
| Cox M. A. | 35 | Staff Nurse | NK | 07/02/19 | |
| Elliott E. | 24 | Nurse | NK | 27/10/18 | |
| Elliott L. M. | 32 | Nurse | NK | 02/03/20 | |
| Flintoff A. | NK | Sister | NK | 09/11/18 | |
| Forbes B. G. F | NK | Staff Nurse | NK | 12/05/18 | |
| Garlick H. M. | 43 | Staff Nurse | Sickness | 12/08/17 | |
| Goldsmith A. A. V. | 32 | Staff Nurse | NK | 05/03/18 | |
| Greatorex J. M. | 38 | Sister | Phthisis | 02/04/16 | |
| Griffin L. | NK | Sister | Died at sea | 05/09/16 | |
| Hastings H. M. | NK | Sister | NK | 23/07/18 | |
| Hills M. E. | 43 | Sister | Sickness | 22/07/18 | |
| Howard F. G. | NK | Staff Nurse | NK | 18/11/14 | |
| Humphrey E. M. | Nk | Sister | NK | 19/04/20 | |
| Irwin W. H. | NK | Staff Nurse | NK | 18/11/18 | |
| Jamieson J. S. | 30 | Staff Nurse | Pneumonia | 30/12/18 | |
| Jinks M. | 28 | Nurse | NK | 29/09/19 | |
| Kemp E. M. | NK | Sister | NK | 20/10/17 | |
| Kerr M. T. | 31 | Staff Nurse | NK | 17/01/15 | |
| Lancaster A. H. | 35 | Nurse | Drowned | 03/06/18 | |
| MacKinnon M. | 31 | Staff Nurse | Drowned *Glenart* | 26/02/18 | |
| McCombie C. | 25 | Nurse | NK | 15/01/19 | |
| Mark H. D. | 23 | Nurse | NK | 10/10/18 | |
| Marley G. M. | 23 | Probationer | NK | 12/10/16 | |
| Marnoch M. B. | 27 | Staff Nurse | NK | 13/11/18 | |
| Meldrum I. | NK | Sister | NK | 02/02/18 | |
| Milne M. L. | NK | Sister | NK | 02/10/17 | |
| Murray M. | 35 | Staff Nurse | Influenza | 02/11/18 | |
| Nodder R. M. | 33 | Nurse | Sickness | 24/05/18 | |
| O'Gorman E. M. | 42 | Sister | Appendicitis | 20/11/14 | |
| Paterson J. J, | 34 | Staff Nurse | NK | 29/09/16 | |
| Robinson E. | NK | Sister | Malaria | 12/07/19 | |
| Rowlands H. M. | 26 | Nurse | Scarlet fever | 10/05/19 | |
| Saxon E. | 26 | Staff Nurse | NK | 03/09/17 | |
| Simpson E. | NK | Nurse | NK | 10/05/17 | |
| Smith C. | NK | Staff Nurse | NK | 26/01/20 | |
| Smithies E. L. | 42 | Staff Nurse | Sickness | 22/02/19 | |
| Stanley A. | 46 | Staff Nurse | NK | 22/12/15 | |
| Stewart W. B. | NK | Staff Nurse | Phthisis | 10/07/18 | |
| Swain L. M. | NK | Staff Nurse | NK | 31/08/15 | |
| Thompson M. B. | 45 | Staff Nurse | Sickness | 18/09/14 | |
| Trevethan R. | NK | Staff Nurse | NK | 04/09/17 | |
| Vinter B. | NK | Staff Nurse | NK | 30/05/18 | |
| Wakefield J. E. | 39 | Sister | NK | 07/02/19 | |

## Territorial Nursing Service (cont.)

| | | | | | |
|---|---|---|---|---|---|
| Watson D. | NK | Staff Nurse | NK | 13/03/17 | |
| Wheatley A. | 48 | Sister | NK | 01/08/19 | |
| Willis F. A. | NK | Sister | NK | 15/12/19 | |
| Wills M. E. | 33 | Staff Nurse | NK | 30/03/18 | |
| Woodley A. A. | 32 | Sister | NK | 10/01/18 | |

## Voluntary Aid Detachment

| Name | Age | Status | Cause | Date | Distinction |
|---|---|---|---|---|---|
| Arnold M. T. | 31 | Nurse | Disease | 12/03/16 | |
| Bailey W. | NK | Nurse | NK | 23/09/18 | |
| Ball C. | 28 | Sister | Drowned *Osmanieh* | 31/12/17 | |
| Barker E. F. | 49 | Nurse | Meningitis | 03/04/18 | |
| Baron M. A. | 28 | Nurse | NK | 22/10/18 | |
| Barrett S. V. | NK | Nurse | Drowned *Leinster* | 10/10/18 | |
| Bartlett B. | 23 | Nurse | Pneumonia | 03/12/18 | |
| Bates M. E. | 35 | Sister | Enemy air raid | 22/12/17 | |
| Bousfield M. C. | 27 | Nurse | Pneumonia | 24/02/19 | MiD |
| Bowser I. T. | NK | Sister | NK | 11/01/19 | OStJJ |
| Brown W. M. | 30 | Sister | Drowned *Osmanieh* | 31/12/17 | |
| Bytheway G. | 37 | Sister | Drowned *Osmanieh* | 31/12/17 | |
| Chadwick M. E. | NK | Nurse | Enteric | 15/10/15 | |
| Chadwick H. | NK | Nurse | NK | 02/11/18 | |
| Chapman M. D. | 27 | Nurse | NK | 10/08/18 | |
| Crewdson D. M. L. | 32 | Sister | Disease | 12/03/19 | |
| Dickson M. | 30 | Nurse | Meningitis | 16/02/17 | |
| Duncanson U. M. | 25 | Nurse | Drowned *Osmanieh* | 31/12/17 | |
| Faithfull F. M. | 26 | Nurse | Drowned | 15/01/18 | |
| Fraser M. N. | NK | Nurse | Typhus | 08/03/15 | |
| Hackett V. C. H. | NK | Nurse | NK | 13/10/18 | |
| Hallam A. V. | 45 | Sister | NK | 18/12/16 | |
| Harding I. L. | 22 | Nurse | Pneumonia | 15/02/19 | |
| Heritage A. | 17 | Nurse | Pneumonia | 31/10/18 | |
| Horrell D. M. | 22 | Nurse | NK | 09/01/21 | |
| Ingram E. | 31 | Nurse | NK | 14/08/18 | |
| Jones L. K. | NK | Nurse | NK | 06/06/16 | |
| Kinnear K. F. | 29 | Nurse | Enteric | 03/09/17 | |
| Lambarde B. A. | 29 | Nurse | NK | 05/03/19 | |
| Langdale M. A. | 39 | Nurse | NK | 09/02/17 | |
| Liddell L. | NK | Nurse | NK | 29/09/18 | |
| Llewellyn G. V. | 19 | Nurse | Influenza | 03/11/18 | |
| Maltey P. M. | 27 | Nurse | Pneumonia | 06/12/18 | |
| Maunsell M. J. | NK | Nurse | NK | 07/01/19 | |
| Midwood L. | 32 | Nurse | Drowned *Osmanieh* | 31/12/17 | |
| Palmieri A. | NK | Nurse | NK | 15/05/17 | |
| Parrott A. M. A. | 37 | Sister | NK | 24/10/18 | |
| Pope C. M. L. | 31 | Sister | NK | 25/06/21 | |
| Powers-Peel A. | NK | Nurse | NK | 31/12/18 | |
| Richards E. | 31 | Nurse | NK | 14/10/18 | |
| Rogers H. A. | 22 | Nurse | Drowned *Osmanieh* | 31/12/17 | |
| Roskell G. L. | 38 | Nurse | Appendicitis | 31/10/15 | |
| Ryle M. C. | NK | Nurse | NK | 21/02/15 | |
| Smales F. E. | NK | Nurse | NK | 13/10/15 | |
| Smith Lee J. | 25 | Nurse | Sickness | 30/03/17 | |
| Thomson E. | NK | Nurse | NK | 30/09/17 | |

**Voluntary Aid Detachment (cont.)**

| Williams J. | 45 | Nurse | NK | 31/01/19 | |
|---|---|---|---|---|---|
| Young A. E. | 33 | Nurse | NK | 15/07/18 | |
| Young M. A. E. | 35 | Nurse | Pneumonia | 13/02/19 | |
| Young M. C. | 25 | Nurse | Disease | 30/07/18 | |

| Deaths by Status | |
|---|---|
| Chief Matrons | 1 |
| Matrons | 9 |
| Assistant Matrons | 2 |
| Sisters | 172 |
| Staff Nurses | 113 |
| Nurses | 68 |
| Assistant Nurses | 1 |
| Probationers | 7 |
| **Total** | **373** |

| Deaths by Year | |
|---|---|
| 1914 | 4 |
| 1915 | 39 |
| 1916 | 41 |
| 1917 | 54 |
| 1918 | 161 |
| 1919 | 53 |
| 1920 | 14 |
| 1921 | 7 |
| **Total** | **373** |

Note: As the dead of the Great War are named in the National Books of Remembrance at War Memorials, the names of those listed above are in the public domain. The author therefore sees no breach of ethics in naming them.

An additional 30 names have been found of nurses who died in service. However, they have not been included in the above table because of insufficient detail.

Source: Commonwealth War Graves Commission, Database of All Female Casualties - Great War, 2001.